MAN AND THE FUTURE

JAMES E. GUNN, EDITOR | MAI

The University Press of Kansas
Lawrence | London

ND THE FUTURE

PREFACE

The concept of an "Inter-Century Seminar" won immediate acceptance from everyone involved in planning the centennial celebration at the University of Kansas. After a splendid hundred years, the University was not so much interested in looking back as in looking ahead to a challenging future. And to celebrate the hundredth anniversary of the founding of a university with what the program chairman called "a feast of ideas" seemed uniquely appropriate.

The Seminar's essays and comments, revised and sharpened for book publication, are thoughtful presentations of lively, mature minds. The reader soon will realize that he is not reading merely the transcription of a seminar: the essays and comments which follow all but the introduction and closing essay possess a remarkable unity. Several factors contributed to this unity. First, the Seminar leaders were asked to address themselves to a single theme, "Man and the Future." Second, the Seminar was planned to be a continuous event, not a series of lectures scattered over a period of months, and the participants were asked to be present for the entire three-and-a-half-day period—to immerse themselves in the task of defining the future of man according to their own disciplines and perceptions. They were asked to present papers about the future of their disciplines and the impacts of those disciplines on mankind, and to serve on panels which discussed each paper immediately after its presentation—to analyze, to question, and sometimes to disagree.

To give life to this format, leaders of world-wide stature were assembled. They were selected because they had distinguished themselves in their fields, because they had demonstrated a gift for prophecy, and because they had a message or a point of view to lay before a broad audience. The reader may wish to read their credentials in the biographical sketches at the end of the book.

Man and the Future begins with an essay by Deane W. Malott, which provides a setting for the Seminar. As Chancellor of the University of Kansas from 1939-1951, he was asked to take a historical perspective, to look at the forces and people that had brought the University to this point.

In his poetic essay, anthropologist Loren Eiseley considers the present condition of man, the problem of prophecy, and the challenge of knowing. Scientist and *Science* editor Philip Abelson provides scale-and-balance estimates of man's resources, scientific expectations, and social and scientific problems.

Retired Supreme Court Justice Charles Whittaker presents his views of the ways in which the meanings of words have been changed, and the implications for man and law and disobedience. Inventor and idea-shaker R. Buckminster Fuller presents a Dymaxion world view as he analyzes man in relation to his environment, from a Fullerized past to a Geodesic future.

World-lawyer Arthur Larson describes the fallacies that handicap men's thinking about international relationships, and speculates about the ways in which the application of the scientific method might change our world outlook. Actor-writer-director Harold Clurman reminisces about the theater, analyzes what it means to men and their society, and prophesies about its future.

Psychiatrist Karl Menninger discusses the irrational manner in which society regards and deals with those who break its laws, and outlines a more reasonable approach to crime and criminals which he believes would result in greater rehabilitation. Science popularizer and science fiction author Arthur C. Clarke ranges well into the future that he has examined so thoroughly in imagination, exploring outer space, how we can expect to get there, how we can expect to live there, and what we can expect to find there; inner space, the oceans and their riches; and automation, with the promise and threat of ultra-intelligent machines.

Finally Franklin D. Murphy, another former Chancellor of the University of Kansas, from 1951-1960, describes how the conditions affecting higher education have changed the nation's universities and the way in which universities will continue to change.

Woven through the comments which follow the eight central essays the reader will find the ideas of these participants further developed and expanded, and he may take some pleasure in tracing threads of continuity. Alongside the comments of the leaders he will find the contributions of a group of critic-commentators, whose spontaneous reactions add much to the elucidation and development of the original presentations: Associated Press science writer Alton Blakeslee; engineering editor Waldo Bowman; author, editor, and now educator Eric Larrabee; anthropologist and social critic Ashley Montagu; astronomer Harlow Shapley; and television critic Robert Lewis Shayon.

A complete analysis of the future was not intended and will not be found in this book; rather the opportunity was presented knowledgeable, perceptive men to speculate freely and boldly about the future. The reader will find, never-

viii |

theless, that the essays explore many of the central issues,
ideas, and techniques which will determine the shape of the
future, if not of man himself.

James E. Gunn
Lawrence, Kansas
August 4, 1967

ACKNOWLEDGMENTS

The Inter-Century Seminar was the brain-child of Prof. William A. Conboy, chairman of the department of speech and drama at the University of Kansas and chairman of the Program Subcommittee of its Centennial Observance Committee. He not only got things going; he kept them going. Other members of the Program Subcommittee who deserve special thanks for their willing contributions of time, ideas, and effort are Prof. Oscar Haugh of the School of Education; Prof. Raymond Hopponen of the School of Pharmacy; Prof. Clayton Krehbiel of the School of Fine Arts; Prof. Donald Metzler of the School of Engineering; James Prager and Deanell Reece, students; Prof. Paul Roofe of the department of zoology; Prof. Earl Shurtz of the School of Law; and Prof. Jack Walker of the School of Medicine. The editor of this volume was also involved in planning and executing the centennial celebration.

Other members of the Centennial Observance Committee who provided ideas, support, and general supervision were Thomas Buckman, Director of Libraries; Frank Burge, Director of the Kansas Union; Prof. J. Neale Carman of the department of French and Italian; Prof. W. Eugene George, Chairman of the department of architecture; Dean Thomas Gorton of the School of Fine Arts; Prof. Bruce Linton, chairman of Radio-Television-Film; Prof. John Nelson of the department of English; Prof. Calder Pickett of the School of Journalism; and student members T. J. Snyder, Kay Orth, William L. Robinson, Jon Putnam, Robert J. Woody, Jeffrey O. Ellis, and David H. Sivright.

Special credit should go to Dick Wintermote, executive director of the Alumni Association, who served as secretary to the Committee and kept everyone informed; to Prof. Natalie Calderwood of the department of English, who headed its Heritage and Traditions Subcommittee; and to Prof. Keith Weltmer, chairman of the Ways and Means Subcommittee, who saw to it that the bills were paid.

And, of course, a major share of the credit for the success of the celebration must go to two men; to Prof. George Anderson, chairman of the history department and chairman of the Centennial Observance Committee, who kept a committee together and working together toward a single objective for two years, and to Chancellor W. Clarke Wescoe, whose enthusiasm, suggestions, and general support made it all possible in the first place and carried it through to its successful conclusion.

J.E.G.

CONTENTS

MAN AND THE FUTURE | **INTRODUCTION**

THE SETTING:
CENTENNIAL AT KANSAS

Deane W. Malott

Far back down the channel of the years, forgetting for our purposes such transients as Coronado, were the Santa Fe and the Oregon trails, which peeled off a certain increment of pioneer spirits from the onward trek to the gold fields, to begin the taming of the almost limitless prairies of the Mid-West.

It took, however, the sharp division and the emotional biases of the slavery question to bring the real pioneers to the Kansas plains; propelled from the East and across the borders from Missouri, baited by the implications first of the Missouri Compromise, and then of the Kansas-Nebraska Act of 1854, signaling, in effect, a free-for-all prelude to the Civil War. Squatter sovereignty in the course of these early years became arrayed, in cruel guerrilla warfare, against the considerable forces of the New England Emigrant Aid Company, under the indomitable energy of Amos Lawrence. The first band left Boston in 1854, marching and singing words of one of Whittier's "Lays of the Emigrants" to the tune of "Auld Lang Syne."

The early days of Kansas were stormy indeed, and there was a good deal of skullduggery about; those in high places were not above a "deal," resulting ofttimes in a handsome profit to themselves, as they worked both in behalf of their constituencies and the growth of their personal power.

There was, of course, a commonly held belief that Kansas was founded in behalf of a cause, which gave it the aura of the preeminent battleground for freedom, something out of the ordinary in the great westward march of more than a hundred years ago. As Carl Becker describes the thinking of the populace in his famous essay on Kansas, "The people of Iowa and Nebraska are well enough, but their history has never brought them in touch with cosmic processes. The Pilgrims themselves are felt to have been actuated by less noble and altruistic motives" than those which caused the westward migrations to the Kansas Territory.

While it is perfectly clear that idealism was only a part of the motivation which brought crusaders pouring into Kansas, those who came actually expected to better their personal opportunities, a fact often pointed out to me a quarter-century ago by Amos Lawrence's son, the Rt. Reverend William Lawrence, long the venerable Episcopal Bishop of Massachusetts.

But in the midst of both practical and ideal matters, most of the leaders in early Kansas went straightway into politics, an area of activity which has always been to the liking of Kansas people. Their propensity in this direction was never better shown than in the early bickering over a capital site. Successive capital locations were pressured into being, first in Leavenworth; then Shawnee Mission; Pawnee —out where the Smoky Hill joins the Republican River; an abortive attempt in a place called Minneola; Lecompton; and, after 1861, of course, Topeka.

By then the good citizens began to look forward to a more stable society. The earliest settlers of Kansas, as someone has said, "had no sooner driven down their tent-pins than they began to talk of a college." Amos Lawrence wrote to Dr. Robinson from Boston about the matter as early as 1854, although he was inclined at first to concentrate upon a boys' preparatory school. No girls, for as he expressed it: "My own impression is that we have fallen into a great error here in Massachusetts of late years, by raising the standard of female education so high that physical development has been checked and their constitutions weakened."

At that time, Amos Lawrence had already depleted his financial resources in a loan to Lawrence College in Appleton, Wisconsin, but by some sort of fiscal legerdemain he pledged the note he received in the Appleton transaction to the Kansas project, to establish "Free State College" in Lawrence. It was to be under the immediate control of the Presbyterian Church, with a board of highly reverend, and somewhat impractical, gentlemen. A lady described as of "boundless energy" was already at work in the East raising money, and the Territorial Legislature of 1859 gave legal sanction for the establishment of Lawrence University. Other church denominations muscled into the activity— it was already a complicated situation—while the reverend gentlemen quietly established chairs in Biblical literature and moral philosophy, Greek and Latin language and literature, English literature, natural science, modern languages, and other disciplines; and established the office of Principal to reign over the female department. But progress was slow, clumsy, and argumentative. By 1859, there was a proposition to establish in Lawrence an institution known as "Monumental College," conceived to commemorate for all time the triumph of liberty over slavery in Kansas. Amos Lawrence and his collateral notes went along with these developments, but uneasiness continued to reign between the Presbyterians and the Congregationalists, thus affording an opportunity for the Episcopalians to enter the discussions, girded for battle. Charters were created in rapid suc-

cession and went down to defeat through the fiscal inadequacies of their proponents. In 1861, the Territorial Legislature gave birth to "Lawrence University of Kansas" (another name for the embryonic institution), at which time
the Presbyterians finally withdrew, and the Episcopalians
gained the ascendancy, under the leadership of the Reverend R. W. Oliver, who became our first, and only, part-
time chancellor—and talked the Episcopalians out of their
money, in behalf of a non-sectarian institution. After this,
the little frontier town of Lawrence settled down, with minor
interruptions such as Quantrill's raid, to become the chief
center of the intellect for the western plains.

Kansas was admitted to the Union in 1861, under a
charter with constitutional provisions for a state university.
Governor Robinson, long identified with the Lawrence community, had to veto a legislative enactment to establish the
institution in Manhattan, where the Methodists already
had Bluemont College as a going operation. Perhaps the
good governor was also motivated by the offer of the city
of Lawrence to provide $15,000 of endowment.

At any rate, by 1864 things had progressed sufficiently
for the Legislature to pass a law to organize the University,
with total resources of just over $10,000.

By 1865, North College was under construction, as a
result of further financial juggling, and three professors were
hired, among them the bouncy and energetic Francis
Huntington Snow. Twenty-six young ladies and twenty-
nine young gentlemen appeared in September of 1866, all
being found unqualified for any but the preparatory department.

At the end of the year Chancellor Oliver had had
enough; he jumped into bed and pulled the covers over his
head by becoming a professor of divinity in a small college

in Nebraska, remaining through the years, however, a staunch friend of K.U.

In late December of 1867, General John Fraser became the first real administrator of the University, at the stupendous salary of $3,000 a year. For this, the doughty general left the presidency of the Agricultural College in Pennsylvania. With consummate energy, he set to work to expand the facilities onto the larger campus lying back of and higher than North College. With great courage and foresight a great new building, largest academic building in all America, was built, on various financial shoestrings that became riotously entangled; and even after its supposed completion, Chancellor Fraser complained that the building, later to bear his name, was so inadequately finished that "the cold air of winter finds free ingress into the building."

General Fraser was a man of great momentum and vigor, but a fiery Scotch disposition shortened his tenure of office. He did, however, last through the first commencement, on June 11, 1873. For that ceremony the famous Senator John J. Ingalls gave the oration, and was completely carried away with the whole occasion, as he thundered about these new "Pilgrim Fathers of the West," impelled "by the unconquerable mind and freedom's holy flame. . . . This," said he in conclusion, "is the State's consummate hour."

Chancellor Fraser was a born promoter, who felt it necessary to make a case for legislative support by citing the steady growth in student attendance. In his enthusiasm he seems to have padded the enrollment figures to such a considerable extent that the faculty found it necessary to correct his statistics.

Next elected as chancellor was a professor of logic from Wisconsin named Carpenter, who duly arrived in Lawrence, took one look around, and immediately departed, never to appear again. A gentleman with the unlikely name of Thwing was elected to the chancellorship. He dawdled over the idea for some time, and then declined the office.

All of which, happening in the rapidly strengthening life stream of the University, shows beyond doubt or peradventure that chancellors are not terribly important, although it has been alleged that deans are occasionally useful. Hence, I shall dwell no more on the University's eleven chancellors, except to venture that Francis Huntington Snow was the greatest leader in the century-long history of the institution, not so much by virtue of his office, as by his sprightly mind, his indefatigable love for collecting books and bugs and birds and stones and plants, his wholesome respect for the out-of-doors, his love of his fellow men, his instinctive judgment, the high quality of his unerring scholarship, and his sense of humor.

The faculty of the University has given stature to the institution from the very beginning. Carefully selected by the educated and idealistic leadership which came to Kansas during the turmoil over slavery, the University, from the moment of its start, has represented the state at its very best. The first faculty held an exalted view of what a university could mean in the life of a pioneer area; their plans now seem somewhat grandiose in the light of the conditions of the day on these frontier prairies. Living in a primitive academic community, they nevertheless clearly hoped to create on the edge of the plains another Harvard or Yale. They were a combination of venturesome leaders, yet grounded in conservative educational opinions. To their initial way of thinking, training in the Greek and Roman classics insured the sound development of the individual, and was the proper educational pattern for a civilized society. So strong was this conviction that when, in the 1880's, a young teacher and former student, William Herbert Carruth, proposed that German be allowed as a substitute for part of the Greek requirement, he was promptly put down very vigorously by his elders.

Yet such was the ruggedness of these early days that they were able to adapt and adjust to the needs of the state. In the rapid succession of the years, they drew away from, indeed outgrew, their Ivy League concept, and gained rapid insight into the needs of a frontier state, so different from the New England campuses of their heritage. One of the first lessons of their rugged experience was to distinguish the fact that the faculty of the burgeoning University was responsible not so much to a board of trustees or an alumni body, as to the whole body of citizens, and it was to these latter that an accounting must be rendered. In turn, the citizens, through the decades of the century, have been increasingly proud of their very own University atop and around its Mt. Oread hill.

In its early recognition of its new responsibilities, the University was undertaking, as early as the 1890's, in addition to its expanding curriculum, all sorts of services to the state. It became the authorized agency for the analysis of foods and drugs; its chancellor was the sealer of weights and measure; it supervised the control of insects; it undertook the study of underground resources; and it early created a curricular division known as "University Extension," to bring cultural and intellectual offerings into the Kansas communities, and to furnish, by mail, instruction in a wide variety of subjects. Full professors and department heads participated actively in these extension programs.

The sturdy determination to carve out its own destiny was also evident by the way in which the University responded to the demands made upon it in the development of scientific programs, in addition to the traditional classical studies. An engineering professor joined the University as early as 1869, and by the 1890's it was reported by the press that the University of Kansas was the only institution in the West where electrical engineering, then reportedly the greatest of all sciences, could be thoroughly studied.

We have long laid claim to a higher proportion of engineering alumni represented in *Who's Who in Engineering* than any university in the Middle West, and it has been further claimed that we have been first among all state universities and colleges in the proportion of our graduates starred in *American Men of Science*.

The latter evidence shows both ability to depart from the traditional, as well as to preserve a sense of academic distinction. Phi Beta Kappa and Sigma Xi entered the campus in 1890. It was the first chapter of each to appear west of the Mississippi; the first of Sigma Xi to appear in a state university, and only the fourth chapter of that organization in the entire country. The University of Kansas was a very early member of the Association of American Universities, attesting to its high caliber of graduate work.

While the University was growing and learning to contribute its talents in many directions for the benefit of the growing state, Kansas itself was also rapidly expanding its functions to meet its obligations to its citizens. Within a short fifty years after its admission to the Union, Kansas had thrown off most of its pioneer ways, and had begun to encounter the kind of economic, social, and political problems which belong to a settled society. Very early the state became relatively progressive in coping with the difficulties of its citizens—the ill, the impoverished, the handicapped, the criminal, and the aged. The same vigorous and resolute qualities were brought to bear as were so evident in the building of the University. Much of the legislation of the state concerned the human needs of all of its citizens; and it quickly adopted the practice, expanded through all the years, of utilizing administrative boards, commissions, councils, and committees to deal with social problems. Particularly have these come into being since the turn of the century. Through this commission structure the state has been able to call upon the ablest of its citizens, largely for volunteer work, and, furthermore, thus to enlist more and more of its people into the structure of government so essential to a democratic society.

The University of Kansas has been a sturdy leader in the evolvement of a distinctively American type of institution—the full-scale state university, unique in the breadth and the scope of its work, and unique in service to a large constituency. The University has always been concerned with the intellectual development of the individual student, with the acquisition and dissemination of knowledge, and with exploration along the vast frontiers of human inquiry.

But our University attempts more than this. Its interest, as a public institution, spreads into fields which, before the 1860's, were not considered the domain of higher education. It learned to deal not only with the problems of theoretical physics, but it also reached out and touched the lives of clerks and farmers, of road builders, and of truck drivers. It has not only trained historians, but has something of value to offer for the firefighter and the highway patrolman.

Today, it still lays stress on metaphysics, but it also serves as a testing center for the maladjusted child. It reaches the housewife in her home, and its radio voice comes to the driver of the tractor, as he works. This not only helps the individual to understand himself, his neighbors, and his country, but it also offers him the opportunity to learn of men in primitive societies.

It provides medical and other professional staffs for the hospitals of the state. The medical school arose out of the charter granted the University in 1864; pre-medical instruc-

tion began in 1879; a two-year medical course was begun
in 1899; and the full school was implemented in 1905. Its
splendid teaching staff and physical plant today place it
as one of the top medical schools in the nation.

The University also provides lawyers to staff the law
courts of the state, and to provide their practitioners. It
supplies research agencies with personnel, the many branches
of state government with myriad specialized workers. It
also offers training to the county clerk, the tax assessor, and
the laboratory technician.

It touches society on a thousand fronts. Not a large
university, as state universities have become, its value re-
sides rather in the scale of its resources, its capacity for
specialized teamwork, the tremendous variety of the skills
which are at its beck and call—in short, its vast resources to
serve all of the people.

And this is an essential service in a day when our whole
cultural heritage is in such precarious balance. A formidable
army of tantalizing problems besets us: our population is
increasing and coagulating in cities; poverty is seen as a
threat to world security; large and small wars and revolutions beset us; there are cultural and racial conflicts on a
world-wide front; and a resurgent nationalism is all too frequently confused with the threat of Communism. K.U.
must be on the forefront of every surge of the modern day.

The University also has stood sturdily apart from most
of its fellow state universities, by vigorously soliciting private, as well as public support. At Chancellor Strong's in-
auguration in 1902, Francis Huntington Snow mentioned
that three buildings had already been built by private funds.
The Kansas University Endowment Association was incorporated in July of 1893, and through the years has become a powerful arm of University support, although private
funds stream in to the University directly, as well as through

the Association. In the last quarter century, private gifts have provided twenty-nine buildings, wholly or in significant part, on Mt. Oread and the Kansas City campus, and nearly seven hundred acres have been added to the University grounds. Furthermore, in the last five years, private support for the University of Kansas has totaled just under sixteen million dollars, significant help to the generous support of the taxpayers of Kansas.

May I emphasize again that this University has been built through the years by the sturdy courage and indomitable will of many men and women—people of high integrity, of great adaptability, and of forthright daring. In long procession through the years they have come and gone, shadowy figures now, but they added, bit by bit, to the distinctive stature and service of the University of Kansas. I have known the vast majority of them since I first climbed Mt. Oread just fifty years ago. They were vibrant people, undaunted by grasshoppers or chinch bugs, or by dust storms, or by lean years of depression, or by salary cuts.

They insisted that the University of Kansas be free to have blowing through it every wind of social, economic, political, and physical change. They have brought here thinkers like Ralph Waldo Emerson; activists like Susan B. Anthony and Lucy Stone; people from the world of affairs like Ulysses S. Grant and William Howard Taft and William Jennings Bryan; educators like President Hadley of Yale and Benjamin Ide Wheeler of the University of California. The University of Kansas has been always a meeting place, a place for free and vigorous espousal and dissent, in the fast moving world of ideas.

Great credit for this spirit of freedom lies in the fact that Kansas has had through the years, with only occasional lapses in stature, a Board of Regents composed of unselfish and high-minded men and women, who understand higher education and are inordinately proud of our state-supported institutions.

And so now we open the Centennial Celebration. It is not the first anniversary celebration in its long history. In 1891, the twenty-fifth was celebrated. Dr. Angell, the President of the University of Michigan, delivered a ringing oration for the occasion.

In 1916 we were already within the shadow of a world war, and nothing was attempted for the semi-centennial beyond an alumni telephone hookup, connecting a group in New York and a group in San Francisco with an audience of a few hundred gathered here in Robinson Gymnasium, during which were exchanged the usual amenities, and Governor Capper was importuned to give the University more funds.

I was here at the time of the diamond jubilee in 1941. The only lasting result of that occasion as I now recall was that Mary Pickford, attending a reunion dinner in the Union building, was asked to give to the University the gown she wore on that occasion, which she subsequently did. There was some thought that it might be stuffed and put in with Comanche but nothing came of the idea; however it must be around here somewhere.

Now, on the University's hundredth anniversary, we are tackling the basic subject "Man and the Future," which I hope will take off from the sturdy background of our first century, and, building upon that structure, throw out the challenges that lie before man, his society, and particularly higher education.

For certain it is that only through education, lots of it for many people, can we begin to meet the responsibility to perpetuate the personal and political freedom which we hold so dear.

Assuming the same thrust and daring and integrity which have characterized our first century, and the continued forthright support of the people of Kansas which has given such a solid and sturdy foundation to this institution on Mt. Oread, what are the challenges that lie ahead for our second century of service to man and the future?

Out of the past have come definite trends in education at K.U. We have been an early experimenter, specifically through our Western Civilization requirement, in placing more than the usual responsibility for the learning process upon the individual student. In what directions may this be developed and how may our leadership in this direction be strengthened?

Kansas early recognized the great value and intellectual strength of providing taxpayers' funds for unrestricted and unspecified research, to assure the vigor and prowess of the University's faculty. This is an impetus which must be maintained and which must surely grow in strength and in value throughout the institution's second century.

During the last two decades of the first hundred years, the federal government has entered the area of higher education to provide funds on many fronts for specific projects. What possibly may be, and what probably should be, the directions of this inevitably increasing support in the decades ahead? And what will be the effect upon other sources of support?

What does the crystal ball show to be the future role of the Kansas University Endowment Association, the activities of which Chancellor Wescoe has described as providing the difference between moderate adequacy and high distinction, in the University's service to the state and to its young people?

Under the sobering influences of our puzzling and changing society, young people of student age are insisting everywhere upon being heard, of having a voice in public debate and institutional decisions. How may this urge somehow be dealt with to bring soundness and understanding and cooperation into the exuberance of their desire to participate? It is a trend which will surely continue down the years of the future, and which must be intelligently met.

With increasing leisure on the part of our citizens everywhere, what is our responsibility for continuing education beyond the adolescent years, upon which K.U. has already built so soundly? As great city sprawls become overly crowded, choked by unmanageable traffic, and smothered in toxic fumes, will the cultural heritage of fine music, and art, and drama become less and less a commercial or private philanthropic adventure in these crowded centers, and become more and more the responsibility of our great centers of learning to disseminate to the people? Can our adult population be enticed and challenged into a continuation of the learning process through our system of adult higher education?

Can our increasingly computerized and mechanized university operations continue to provide personal contact with the individual student, that supreme experiment in living, whose stability and character and enterprise is so vital to personal, national, and world freedom? What will, or should be, the future of teaching machines and mechanical aids?

Can we maintain on our campuses a prime focus of the teaching art and its satisfying challenges, and resist the encroachment of too much emphasis upon travel fellowships, consulting opportunities, and the demands of sponsored research, which otherwise could bring us to the point where a faculty appointment provides merely a staging area for a proliferation of outside activities?

How can we be more efficient in organizing the educa-

tional process to handle the increasing spread of knowledge, without at the same time unduly adding years to the
length of the curricula?

These are the sorts of encroaching questions, pressing,
serious, and debatable, which intrude upon our consciousness as this University addresses itself to the topic of "Man
and the Future" during the Inter-Century Seminar.
Whether it be these or other questions which our distinguished participants will be discussing, we face a stimu-
lating experience in the midst of an intriguing subject.

How I should like to be spooking around somewhere a
hundred years hence, to see the fulfillment of our second
century dreams. The University will be here, of that I have
no doubt. I so well remember participating in Harvard
University's Tercentennial in 1936; someone in behalf of
the Harvard Alumni Association had just moved to adjourn
its recurring centennial meeting for another hundred years.
The aging president emeritus of the University, A. Lawrence
Lowell, nephew of our Amos Lawrence, rose to second the
motion, for, said he: "I have observed that institutions never
die, while they are still alive."

The University of Kansas gives every evidence that it
is vitally alive and, with the thrust of this inter-century
celebration, will move confidently, ably, and sturdily into
the second century that lies ahead.

MAN AND THE FUTURE | 1

MAN,
TIME,
and PROPHECY

Loren C. Eiseley

"Former men," observed Emerson, in the dramatic days of the new geological science, "believed in magic, by which temples, cities and men were swallowed up, and all traces of them gone. We are coming on the secret of a magic which sweeps out of men's minds all vestiges of theism and beliefs which they and their fathers held. . . . Nature," he contended clairvoyantly, "is a mutable cloud." Within that cloud is man. He constitutes in truth one of Emerson's most profound questions. Examined closely he is more than a single puzzle. He is an indecipherable palimpsest, a walking document initialed and obscured by the scrawled testimony of a hundred ages. Across his features and written into the very texture of his bones are the half-effaced signatures of what he has been, of what he is, of what he may become.

Modern man lives increasingly in the future and tends to neglect the present. A people who essay to do this have an insatiable demand for soothsayers and oracles to assure and comfort them about the insubstantial road they tread. By contrast, I am a person known very largely, if at all, as one committed to the human past—to the broken columns of lost civilizations, to what can be discovered in the depths of tombs, or dredged from ice-age gravels, or drawn from the features of equally ancient crania. Yet as I go to and fro upon my scientific errands I find that the American public is rarely troubled about these antiquarian matters. Instead, people invariably ask: "What will man be like a million years from now?"—frequently leaning back with complacent confidence as though they already knew the answer but felt that the rituals of our society demanded an equally ritualistic response from a specialist. Or they inquire, as a corollary, what the scientists' views may be upon the colonization of outer space. In short, the cry goes up, "Prophesy!" Before attempting this dubious enterprise, however, I should like to recount the anecdote of a European philosopher who, over a hundred years ago, sensed the beginnings of the modern predicament.

It seems that along a particularly wild and forbidding section of the English coast—a place of moors, diverging and reconverging trackways, hedges, and all manner of unexpected cliffs and obstacles—two English gentlemen were out riding in the cool of the morning. As they rounded a turn in the road they saw a coach bearing down upon them at breakneck speed. The foaming, rearing horses were obviously running wild; the driver on the seat had lost the reins. As the coach thundered by the terrified screams of the occupants could be heard.

The gentlemen halted their thoroughbred mounts and briefly exchanged glances. The same thought seemed to strike each at once. In an instant they set off at a mad gallop which quickly overtook and passed the lurching vehicle before them. On they galloped. They distanced it.

"Quick, the gate!" cried one as they raced up before a hedge. The nearest horseman leaped to the ground and flung wide the gate just as the coach pounded around the curve.

As the swaying desperate driver and his equipage plunged through the opening the man who had lifted the bar shouted to his companion: "Thirty guineas they go over the cliff!"

"Done!" cried his fellow, groping for his wallet.

The gate swung idly behind the vanished coach and the two sporting gentlemen listened minute by minute, clutching their purses. A bee droned idly in the heather and the smell of the sea came up across the moor. No sound came up from below.

There is a strange resemblance in that hundred-year-old story to what we listen for today. We have just opened the gate and the purse is in our hands. The roads on that fierce coast diverge and reconverge. In some strange manner, in a single instant we are both the sporting gentlemen intent on their wager and the terrified occupants of the coach. There is no sound on all this wild upland. Something has happened or is about to happen, but what? The suspense is intolerable. We are literally enduring a future that has not yet culminated, that has, perhaps, been hovering in the air since man arose. The lunging, rocking juggernaut of our civilization has charged by. We wait by minutes, by decades, by centuries, for the crash we have engendered. The strain is in our minds and ears. The betting money never changes hands because there is no report of either safety or disaster. Perhaps the horses are still poised and falling on the great arc of the air.

We shift our feet uneasily and call to the first stranger for a word, a sanctified guess, an act of divination. As among the ancient Greeks, chresmologues, dealers in crumbling parchment and uncertain prophecy, pass among us. I am such a one. But the chresmologue's profession demands that he be alert to signs and portents in both the natural and human worlds—events or sayings that others might regard as trivial but to which the gods may have entrusted momentary meaning, pertinence or power. Such words may be uttered by those unconscious of their significance, casually, as in a bit of overheard conversation between two men idling on a street, or in a bar at midnight. They may also be spoken upon journeys, for it is then that man in the role of the stranger must constantly confront reality and decide his pathway.

It was on such an occasion not long ago that I overheard a statement from a ragged derelict which would have been out of place in any age except, perhaps, that of the Roman twilight and our own time. It was precisely the sort of remark that a knowledgeable Greek would have examined for a god's hidden meaning and because of which a military commander, upon overhearing the words, might have postponed a crucial battle or recast his auguries.

I had come into the smoking compartment of a train at midnight, out of the tumult of a New York week-end. As I settled into a corner I noticed a man with a paper sack a few seats beyond me. He was meager of flesh and his cheeks had already taken on the molding of the skull beneath them. His threadbare clothing suggested that his remaining possessions were contained in the sack poised on his knees. His eyes were closed, his head flung back. He either drowsed from exhaustion or liquor, or both. In that city at midnight there were many like him.

By degrees the train filled and took its way into the dark. After a time the door opened and the conductor shouldered his way in, demanding tickets. I had one sleepy eye fastened on the dead-faced derelict. It is thus one hears from the gods.

"Tickets!" bawled the conductor.

I suppose everyone in the car was watching for the usual thing to occur. What happened was much more terrible.

Slowly the man opened his eyes, a dead man's eyes.

Equally slowly a stick-like arm reached down and fumbled in his pocket, producing a roll of bills. "Give me," he said then, and his voice held the croak of a raven in a church-yard, "give me a ticket to wherever it is."

The conductor groped, stunned, over the bills. The dead eyes closed. The trainman's hastily produced list of stations had no effect. Obviously disliking this role of Charon he selected the price to Philadelphia, thrust the remaining bills into the derelict's indifferent hand and departed. I looked around. People had returned to their papers, or were they only feigning?

In a single sentence that cadaverous individual had epitomized modern time as opposed to Christian time and in the same breath had pronounced the destination of the modern world. One of the most articulate philosophers of the twentieth century, Henri Bergson, has dwelt upon life's indeterminacy, the fact that it seizes upon the immobile, animates, organizes, and hurls it forward into time. In a single poignant expression this shabby creature on a midnight express train had personalized in a breath the terror of an open-ended universe. I know that all the way to Philadelphia I fumbled over my seat check and restudied it doubtfully. It no longer seemed to mean what it indicated. As I left the train I passed the bearer of the message. He slept on, the small brown sack held tightly in his lap. Somewhere down the line the scene would be endlessly repeated. Was he waiting for some final conductor to say "this is the place" at a dark station? Or was there money in the paper sack and had he been traveling for a hundred years in these shabby coaches as a stellar object might similarly wander for ages on the high roads of the night?

All I can assert with confidence is that I was there. I heard the destination asked for, I saw the money taken. I was professionally qualified to recognize an oracle when I heard one. It does not matter that the remark was cryptic. Good prophecy is always given in riddles, for the gods do not reveal their every secret to men. They only open a way and wait for mortal nobility or depravity to take its natural course. "A ticket to wherever it is" carries in the phrase itself the weight of a moral judgment. No civilization professes openly to be unable to declare its destination. In an age like our own, however, there comes a time when individuals in increasing numbers unconsciously seek direction and taste despair. It is then that dead men give back answers and the sense of confusion grows. Soothsayers, like flies, multiply in periods of social chaos. Moreover, let us not confuse ourselves with archaic words. In an age of science the scientist may emerge as a soothsayer.

There is one profound difference which separates psychologically the mind of the classical world from that of the present: the conception of time. The ancient world, to use Frank Manuel's phrase, was bound to the wheel of Ixion, to the maxim: what has been is, passes, and will be. By contrast, the Christian thinkers of western Europe have, until recently, assumed a short time scale of a few millennia. In addition, Christianity replaced the cyclical recurrences of Greek and Roman history by an unreturning concept of the past. History became the drama of the Fall and the Redemption, and therefore, as drama, was forewritten and unrepeatable. Novelty was its essence just as duration and repetition lay at the heart of classical thinking.

Between the earlier conception of time and its reordering in the phrase, what is will *not* be, lies an irredeemable break with the past even though, in the course of two thousand years, much has changed and conceptions derived originally from both realms of thought have interpenetrated. Western philosophy has been altered under the impact of science and become secularized, but history as the eternally new, as "progress," repeats the millenarianism of Christianity. As for the time scale, which modern science has enormously extended, the intuitions of the ancients have proved correct, but biology has contributed an unreturning novelty to the shapes of life. Thus the great play has lengthened and become subject to the mysterious contingencies which are the proper matter of genetics. The play remains, however, just as the anthropologist has similarly demonstrated in the social realm, a performance increasingly strange, diverse, and unreturning. In the light of this distinction, the role of the oracle in the ancient world can be seen to differ from that of his modern analogue, whether the latter be disguised as a science fiction writer, a speculative scientist engaged in rational extrapolation, or a flying saucer enthusiast replacing the outmoded concept of the guardian angel by the guarding intelligence of extraterrestrial beings.

Since emergent creativity, the truly historical character of the living world, went largely unnoticed, the kind of future in which western man now participates was also neglected. Men lived amidst the ruins of past civilization or epochs, indifferently wedging great sculpture or invaluable inscriptions into the wall of a peasant's hut or a sheep corral. Few indeed were the attempts to probe the far future or remote past. Men requested of the oracles what men have always desired: the cure for illness, the outcome of battle, the wisdom or unwisdom of a sea journey, the way to a girl's heart. They asked, in effect, next day's or next year's future because, save for the misfortunes that beset the individual's pathway, all lives and all generations were essentially the same.

There was, in the words of the Old Testament, "nothing new under the sun." The wind went about his circuits, the wave subsided on the beach only to rise again. The generations of men were like the wave—endless but the same. It was a wave of microcosmic futures, the difference between the emperor in purple and the slave under the lash. Each man was mortal; roles could be reversed and sometimes were. This was important to the buffeted individual but not to the wave. Men's individual fates resembled the little dance of particles under the microscope, which we call the Brownian movement.

Perhaps, over vaster ranges of time than man has yet endured, the dance of civilizations may seem as insignificant. Indeed it must have seemed so intuitively to the ancients for, in the endless rising and falling of the wave, lost palace and lost throne would all come round again. It was of little use, therefore, to trouble one's heart over the indecipherable inscription on a fallen monument. Let the immortal gods on the mountain keep their own accounts. In the sharp cold of midwinter one asked only if next year's pastures would be green.

But with the agony in the garden at Gethsemane came the concern for last things, for the end of the story of man. A solitary individual, one who prayed sleepless that his fate might pass, had spoken before the Pharisees, "I know whence I have come and whither I am going." No man had said such a thing before and none would do so after him. For our purpose, it does not matter what we believe or disbelieve; whether we are pagan, Jew, Christian, or Marxist. The voice and the words were those of a world-changer.

At the place Golgotha they say the earth shook. It is true in retrospect, for the mind of western man was there shaken to its foundation. It had gained the courage to ask the final terrible question, for what end was it made? Not the insignificant queries long addressed to wandering magicians, but such a question as a man could ask only in a desert: *what is the end?* Not of me, not of my neighbor or my generation, but the end of man. For what was the lime engendered in our bones, our bodies made to rise in the bright sun and again in dust to be laid down? It may well be that rocks were torn when that cry escaped on human breath. With it man had entered unknowingly upon history, upon limitless time, and equally limitless change. Nothing would be what it had been. The wave would fall no longer idly on the shore. It would loom vaster, bluer, darker until lightning played along its summit, the deepest, most dangerous wave in the entire universe—the wave of man.

The play upon which man had entered would at first be confined to a tiny immovable stage. Its acts would be centered within the brief time span then humanly conceivable. The very compression and foreshortening thus achieved, however, would heighten the intensity of the drama and whet man's concern with the unique course of events. The ancient cyclical conceptions of the pagan world would seem wearisome and banal, its gods without dignity. By contrast, an historic event, the mallet strokes upon a hill outside Jerusalem, would echo in men's minds across nineteen hundred years.

The Crucifixion was not an act that could be re-endured perpetually. "God forbid," wrote St. Augustine, "that we should believe this. Christ died once for our sins, and, rising again, dies no more." The magnitude of the universe remained unknown, its time depths undiscovered, its evolutionary transformations unguessed. One thing alone had changed: the drama of man's life. It now had force, direction, and significance beyond the purely episodic. The power of a single divinity sustained the stage, the drama, and the actors. Men had arrived at true historicity. Acts of evil and of good would run long shadows out into eternity. Self-examination and self-knowledge would be intensified.

On this scene of increasing cosmic order would also

emerge eventually a heightened interest in nature as a mani-
festation of that same Divinity. In time nature would
be spoken of as the second book of God's revelation. Some
would regard it as the most direct communication of all,
less trammeled by words, less obscured by human contention. There would begin, by degrees, the attentive, innocent
examination that would lead on through doubts and ques-
tionings to the chill reality of the ever-wandering stars, to
time stretched across millions of light years, or read in the
erosion of mountain systems or by virtue of unexpected ap-
paritions in the stratified rocks. Finally, Jean Baptiste
Lamarck, in 1809, the year of Darwin's birth, would venture
dryly, "Doubtless nothing exists but the will of the sublime
Author of all things, but can we set rules for him in the
execution of his will, or fix the routine for him to observe?
Could not his infinite power create an order of things which
gave existence *successively* to all that we see. . . ."

The tragedy on a barren hill in Judea, which for so long
had held human attention, would seem to shrink to a
miniscule event on a sand-grain planet lost in a whirl of
fiery galaxies. Reluctantly men would peer into the hollow
eye sockets of the beasts from which they had sprung. The
Christian dream would linger but the surety of direction
would depart. Nature, the second book of the theologians,
would prove even more difficult of interpretation than the
first. Once launched upon the road into the past, man's
insatiable hunger to devour eternity would grow. He would
seek to live in past, present, and future as one, one eternity
of which he might be the intellectual master.

Over fifty years ago it was possible to catch something
of this feeling in the musings of the archaeologist Arthur
Weigall, wandering in the upper Egyptian deserts. In an
abandoned quarry he came upon many hewn stones addressed, as he says, "to the Caesars, but never dispatched

to them; nor is there anything in this time forsaken valley which so brings the past before one as do these blocks awaiting removal to vanished cities. . . . Presently," he continues, "a door seems to open in the brain. Two thousand years have the value of the merest drop of water."

Like Weigall, the desert wanderer, I have done much walking in my younger years. When I climbed I almost always carried seeds with me in my pocket. Often I liked to carry sunflower seeds, acorns, or any queer "sticktight" that had a way of gripping fur or boot tops as if it had an eye on Himalayas and meant to use the intelligence of others to arrive at them. I have carried such seeds up the sheer walls of mesas, and I have never had illusions that I was any different to them than a grizzly's back or a puma's paw.

They had no interest in us—bear, panther, or man—but they were endowed with a preternatural knowledge that at some point we would lie down and there they would start to grow. I have, however, aided their machinations in a way they could scarcely have intended. I have dropped sunflower seed on stony mesa tops and planted cactus in Alpine meadows amidst the sounds of water and within sight of nodding bluebells. I have sowed northern seeds south and southern seeds north and crammed acorns into the most unlikely places. You can call it a hobby if you like. In a small way I, too, am a world changer and hopefully tampering with the planetary axis. Most of my experiments with the future will come to nothing but some may not.

Life is never fixed and stable. It is always mercurial, rolling and splitting, disappearing and re-emerging in a most unpredictable fashion. I never make a journey to a wood or a mountain without experiencing the temptation to explode a puffball in a new clearing or stopping to encourage some sleepy monster that is just cracking out of the earth mold. It is, of course, an irresponsible attitude since I cannot tell what will come of it, but if the world hangs on such matters it may be well to act boldly and realize all immanent possibilities at once. Shake the seeds out of their pods, I say, launch the milkweed down and set the lizards scuttling. We are in a creative universe. Let us then create. After all, man himself is the unlikely consequence of such forces. In the spring when a breath of wind sets the propellers of the maple seeds to whirring, I always say to myself hopefully "after us the dragons."

To have dragons one must have change; that is the first principle of dragon lore. Otherwise everything becomes stale, commonplace, and observed. I suspect that it is this unimaginative boredom which leads to the vulgar comment that evolution may be all very well as a theory but you can never really see anything in the process of change. There is also the even more obtuse and less defensible attitude of those who speak of the world's creative energies as being exhausted, the animals small and showing no significant signs of advance. "Everything is specialized in blind channels," some scientists contend. "Life is now locked permanently in little roadside pools, or perching dolefully on television aerials."

Such men never pause to think how *they* might have looked gasping fishily through mats of green algae in the Devonian swamps, but that is where the *homunculus* who preceded them had his abode. I have never lost a reverent and profound respect for swamps, even individually induced ones. I remember too well what, on occasion, has come out of them. Only a purblind concern with the present can lead to such attitudes, and it is my contention that a sympathetic observer, even at this moment, can witness such marvels of transitional behavior, such hoverings between the *then* and *now*, as to lay forever to rest the notion that evolution belongs somewhere in the witch world of the past.

One may learn much in those great cemeteries of which Weigall spoke, those desolate Gobis and wind-etched pinnacles that project like monuments out of the waste of time itself. One must learn, however, to balance their weight of shards and bones against a frog's leap, against a crow's voice, against a squeak in the night or something that rustles the foliage and is gone. It is here that the deception lies. The living are never seen like the dead, and the living appear to be so surely what they are. We lack the penetration to see the present and the onrushing future contending for the soft feathers of a flying bird, or a beetle's armor, or shaking painfully the frail confines of the human heart.

We are in the center of the storm and we have lost our sense of direction. It is not out of sadistic malice that I have carried cockleburs out of their orbit, or blown puffball smoke into new worlds. I wanted to see to what vicissitudes they might adapt, or in what mountain meadows the old thorns might pass away. One out of all those seeds may grope forward into the future and writhe out of its current shape. It is similarly so on the windswept uplands of the human mind.

Evolution is far more a part of the unrolling future than it is of the past; for the past, being past, is determined and done. The present, in the words of Karl Heim, "is still in the molten phase of becoming. It is still undecided. It is still being fought for." The man who cannot perceive that battleground looks vaguely at some animal which he expects to transform itself before his eyes. When it does not he shrugs and says, "Evolution is all very well but you cannot see it. Besides it does not direct you. It only teaches you that you are an animal and had better act like one."

Yet even now the thing we are trying to see is manifesting itself. Missing links, partial adaptations, transitions from one environmental world to another, animals caught in slow motion half through some natural barrier are all about us. They literally clamor for our attention. We ourselves are changelings. Like Newton, those who possess the inclination and the vision may play on the vast shores of the universe with the living seeds of future worlds. Who knows, through the course of unimaginable eons, how the great living web may vibrate slightly and give out a note from the hand that plucked it long ago? In the waste dumps at city edges bloom plants that have changed and marched with man across the ages since he sat by hill barrows and munched with the dogs. A hand there, brown with sun, threw a seed and the world altered. Perhaps, in some far meadow, a plant of mine will survive the onset of an age of ice. Perhaps my careless act will root life more firmly in the dying planetary days when man is gone and the last seeds shower gallantly against the frost.

What is true biologically is also true along the peripheries of the mind itself. We possess our own Alpine meadows, excoriating heat and freezing cold. There has been, according to philosophers, political man, religious man, economic man. Today there are, variously, psychological man, technological man, scientific man. Dropped seeds, all of them, the mind's response to its environments, its defense against satiety. He who seeks naïvely to embrace his own time will accept its masks and illusions. The men of one period may turn completely to religious self-examination and become dogmatically contentious. Our own age, by contrast, turns outward as if in the flight from self of which its rockets have become the symbol. It has been well said by Philip Rieff that every personality cure seems to expose man to a new illness. I believe it is because man always choses to rest on his cure.

We have forgotten the greatest injunction of the wise traveler from Galilee. He did not say before the Pharisees,

"I know where I am staying." Instead he observed that he knew where he was going. As is true of all great prophets, he left something unspoken hanging in the air. Men have chosen to assume that Jesus had knowledge of his physical fate or that he was bound to some safe haven beyond mortal reach. It seldom occurs to us that he was definitely engaged on a journey. If, in traveling that road, it led incidentally to a high place called Golgotha, it was because his inward journey was higher and more dangerous still.

Five centuries ago an unknown Christian mystic wrote thus of heaven, which his contemporaries assumed to be a definable place: "Heaven ghostly," he said, "is as high down as up, and up as down: behind as before, before as behind, or one side as another. Insomuch, that whoso had a true desire for to be at heaven, then that same time he were in heaven ghostly. For the high and the next way thither is run by desires and not by paces of feet."

Today our glimpses of heaven have become time projected. They are secular; they are translated into paces measured by decades and centuries. Science is the assumed instrument and progress a dynamic flow, as is the heaven we seek to create or abjure. In final analysis we deceive ourselves. Our very thought, through the experimental method, is outwardly projected upon time and space until it threatens to lose itself, unexamined, in vast distances. It does not perform the contemplative task of inward perception.

The mysterious author of The Cloud of Unknowing spoke rightly and his words apply equally to that future we seek to conjure up. The future is neither ahead nor behind, on one side or another. Nor is it dark or light. It is contained within ourselves; it is drawn from ourselves. Its evil and its good are perpetually within us. The future that we seek from oracles, whether it be war or peace, starvation or plenty, disaster or happiness, is not forward to be come upon. Rather its gestation is now, and from the confrontation of that terrible immediacy we turn away to spatial adventures and to imagination projected forward into time as though the future were fixed, unmalleable to the human will, and only to be come upon as a seventeenth-century voyager might descry, through his spyglass, smoke rising from an unknown isle.

Not so is the human future. It is made of stuff more immediate and inescapable: ourselves. If our thought runs solely outward and away upon the clever vehicles of science, just so will there be in that future the sure intellectual impoverishment and opportunism which flight and anonymity so readily induce. It will be, and this is the difficult obstacle of our semantics, not a future come upon by accident with all its lights and shadows, guiltless as in a foreign sea. It will be instead the product of our errors, hesitations, and escapes, returning inexorably as the future which we only wished to come upon like a geographical discoverer, but to have taken no responsibility in shaping.

If, therefore, it is my occasional task to cast auguries, I will repeat as pertinent the further words of that long vanished seer: "Be wary that thou conceive not bodily, that which is meant ghostly, although it be spoken bodily in bodily words as be these, up or down, in or out, behind or before. This thought may be better felt than seen; for it is full blind and full dark to them that have but little while looked thereupon." If we banish this act of contemplation and contrition from our midst, then even now we are dead men and the future dead with us. For the endurable future is a product not solely of the experimental method or of outward knowledge alone. It is born of compassion. It is born of inward seeing. The unknown one called it simply *All* and he added that it was not in a bodily manner to be wrought.

An old colleague of mine, who was much preoccupied with travel and who suffered from absent-mindedness, once turned timidly to his wife as he set forth upon a long journey. "Is the place where I am going," he asked her anxiously, for he depended much upon her notes of instruction, "in my pocket?" It strikes me now that in few centuries has the way seemed darker or the maps we carry in our separate pockets more contradictory if not indecipherable.

The Russians in their early penetration of space saw fit to observe irreverently that they had not seen heaven or glimpsed the face of God. As for the Americans, in our first effort we could only clamorously exclaim, "Boy, what a ride!" Amidst those words on a newscast, I had opened a window on the night air. It was moonrise. In spite of the cynical Russian pronouncement, my small nephew had just told me solemnly that he had seen God out walking. Concerned as adults always are lest chidren see something best left unseen, I consulted his mother. She thought a moment. Then a smile lighted her face. "I told him God made the sun and the stars," she explained. "Now he thinks that the moon is God."

I went and reasoned gravely with him. The gist of my extemporized remarks came from the medieval seer. "Not up, or down," I cautioned, "nor walking in the sun, nor in the night—above all not that."

There was a moment of deep concentration. An uncertain childish voice reached up to me suddenly. "Then where did God get all the dirt?"

I, in my turn, grew quiet and considered.

"Out of a dark hat in a closet called Night," I parried. "We, too, come from there."

"*Conceive it better as not wrought by hands,*" the voice repeated in my head.

"Then how do we see Him?" the dubious little voice trailed up to me. "Where is He then?"

"He is better felt than seen," I repeated. "We do not look up or down but in here." I touched the boy's heart lightly. "In here is what a great man called simply 'All.' The rest is out there"—I gestured—"and roundabout. It is not nearly so important."

The world was suddenly full of a vast silence. Then upon my ear came a sound of galloping infinitely remote, as though a great coach passed, sustained upon the air. I touched the child's head gently. "We are in something called a civilization," I said, "a kind of wagon with horses. It is running over the black bridge of nothing. If it falls, we fall."

"Thirty guineas," a cricket voice chirped in my brain. I shut it out along with the glimpse of a seacliff in the English fog.

"Conceive it not bodily," the clear voice persisted like a bell, "for it is meant ghostly." From below a hand gave itself up trustingly to mine.

"I saw Him. I did so," said the child.

"We will go and look all about," I comforted, "for that is good to do. But mostly we will look inside, for that is where we ache and where we laugh and where at last we die. I think it is mostly there that He is very close."

We went out side by side a little shyly onto the lawn and watched the stars. After a while, and carefully, being small, we turned and looked for the first time at our two selves. Not bodily, I mean, but ghostly. But being still the wandering chresmologue, I told him about a very ancient

---

"Man, Time, and Prophecy" was originally presented at the University of Kansas in April 1966 and subsequently published in a limited edition by Harcourt, Brace & World, through whose courtesy it is here reprinted.

manuscript in which is dimly written: "wherever thou wilt
thou dost assemble me, and in assembling me thou dost
assemble thyself."

COMMENTARIES

WESCOE: I think we've heard a man who has made his
peace with Nature by realizing how great a part of Nature
he is. I would hope, though, that we never find out
exactly to wherever it is that ticket should be bought.
I doubt we could really tolerate it if we did know. This is
the glory of being a human being, of being alive.

I suspect that is the virtue of the remark of the great traveler.

LARRABEE: I would feel more appropriate following
Loren Eiseley's remarks, the remarks of a poet, with silence
rather than with words. I would rather do nothing but praise
him, rather do nothing but sing the same deeply and
joyously tragic song of exultation in this human dilemma,
and make such remarks that I have to in no other spirit
than that.

The road that led us here is a road lined with a kind
of pride in the human ability to surmount its obstacles, the
human ability to master the dilemmas which science in all its
glory and tragedy has come to symbolize and to represent.

One could wish nothing more of scientists than that all of
them should be like Dr. Eiseley. Yet I can't help feeling,
listening to a scientist saying what he says, as beautifully as he
does, that the scientist enjoys a privilege today denied to many
of the rest of us—I say "rest of us" meaning non-scientists,
humanists, or generalists—that is, to be able to flirt with
mysticism without losing his virginity.

It is an extraordinary thing to behold and yet also, for those others of us who came by that way before, a somewhat unsettling thing, since it forces us back on the obligation to behave in a small-minded way, as we usually accuse the scientist of behaving. And, at the same time I find myself cast, by this position, in the role of being more optimistic about man's creative side, perhaps more convinced about science, than Dr. Eiseley is.

MONTAGU: That last comment of Mr. Larrabee's is exactly my position, because Dr. Eiseley speaks not only as a scientist and an anthropologist but also as a human being. When Mr. Larrabee said that he wished that all scientists were like Dr. Eiseley, I can only echo the sentiment. Unfortunately all scientists are not like Dr. Eiseley, and this is one of the reasons why I consider science far too important to leave in the hands of the scientist.

One of the questions that Dr. Eiseley rhetorically put was, "What is the end of man?" and here his and my own field of endeavor, namely anthropology, I think has a great deal to say, but to which many of our colleagues—those unacknowledged legislators of the world, the anthropologists—have thus far paid very little attention. By virtue of their interest in humanity, they have discovered some of the conditions that have been operative in the development, the evolution, of this highly improbable creature. Some of these conditions are quite new to the realm of science and invoke the use of words not customarily found in the vocabulary of scientists. For example, we have very good reason to believe that this creature could not have survived for any length of time after his expulsion from the Garden of Eden, that is to say from the woodlands, onto the open savannas, had he not developed a way of life which was a highly cooperative one, very unlike the competitive one in which most of our authorities have conditioned us to believe to be the history of man's evolution; and that beyond all other things the ability to love was perhaps the principal factor in enabling this creature to make his way in the world. And this is largely how I interpret the findings of contemporary anthropological investigation. I think this is extremely important for us to understand, because as Aristotle said, "If

we would know what man is born for, it is extremely important
for us first to learn what he is born as," and I think we can
now state quite unequivocally—at any rate for the broad elements
of the picture—that what he is born as is a creature born
to live and love.

EISELEY: May I just remark that as a brother anthropologist
I couldn't agree more with what Dr. Ashley Montagu has
just said.

LARRABEE: I wanted to ask a question about Darwin
but I don't know exactly how to pose it. I think Dr.
Montagu's statement leads directly into it. I'm reminded of
the poem of Robert Frost's about New Hampshire in which he
talks of encountering a farmer in a wagon going in the opposite
direction, and they fall into a conversation. The farmer, like
all farmers in Frost's poems, was terribly well educated, and
they began talking about the Mid-Victorians. The farmer said,
"The matter with the Mid-Victorians seems to have been a man
named John L. Darwin." And Frost says, "Go 'long, said I to
him, he to his horse."
The trouble with the Victorians being Darwin and the
trouble with us still being Darwin, too, came to me listening to
Dr. Eiseley put forward evolution as a principle, as a justification,
almost as a guiding condition of our ultimate destination.
This use of it is in sharp contrast to what Darwinism meant to
many of the people who first adopted it, and it was exactly that
misinterpretation, or divergent interpretation, of Darwinism
that he was speaking against. In the light of what Dr. Eiseley
was saying, the question this raises for me is how we are to
regard a particular piece of science? How are we to consider
where it came from, how are we to consider the kind of impact
it has on our lives, how are we to consider the judgment
rendered on it now, how are we to consider the arguments
which still go on? And to me, to the non-scientist looking at it,
it is a lesson in the inappropriateness of the strictly scientific
interpretation, even of what may seem to be a scientific event.
The Darwinian revolution, certainly in terms of intellectual
impact, is the greatest of the scientific revolutions, the one
which finally established after three hundred years of effort an

indisputable authority of science to speak in matters of physical fact, reality, and theory. This revolution was at the same time something quite different, an event in the literary, in the administrative, in the political lives of the men living at that time, an event embedded in technological developments, in canal digging, in railroad building, in the capability of the steamship to allow men to travel around on the globe and make a catalog of what was on it, all of these things were in the nature of the thing we call the Darwinian Revolution. And to study this now is to study what to me is a humanistic rather than a scientific event.

EISELEY: I think that Mr. Larrabee has made an extremely important point, because no great scientific discovery stands by itself in the sense of remaining totally within the hands of specialists. Whether we will it so or not, ideas radiate outward; they affect thinking in a variety of ways, they are reflected through a variety of temperaments. One only has to look, for example, at the different ways in which social philosophers reacted to Darwinism to realize that what first emerged as a scientific theory or discovery began to transmogrify and modify the thinking of many other people. And this, of course, means that we have to think carefully as scientists and express ourselves with great care, because, even so, there will be distortions, changes. We ourselves may unconsciously lend weight to one aspect of a thought which is perhaps many-faceted and which reflects light from different directions. Man possesses this peculiarity: once he becomes convinced that something is true he begins to act as though it were true. This is why we have to be so careful about the kind of "instincts" that we write into the human substance; unconsciously we may be giving ourselves, through this strange mirror, a shape which we do not possess in terms of human nature but one which we have imposed upon ourselves or which we have allowed our culture to impose. This is why the study of science—not just today's science but the history of transformations of thought which science has undergone—is so important. Because science does not progress down an ever-widening pathway, it has its divergencies, its wanderings, its mistakes. We will understand science only to the extent that we recognize it as a force which not alone affects our lives but which, in turn, also influences the scientist himself in terms of his own time and his own society and its beliefs. If we understand this much we will be, perhaps, a little more sophisticated in what we think about ourselves, and to that degree we will be capable of that eternal travel, with some sense of direction, of which I spoke.

BLAKESLEE: I should like to ask Dr. Eiseley just how desperate is man's situation today? How much leeway do we have in learning how to control our feelings, or in using these vast powers that we learn by understanding more about the atom, or other sources of energy? Has man improved in his ability to accept new ideas? Sir Wilfred Trotter, a British physician, once described a new idea as an antigen—which in medical terms is something that instigates antibodies of defense. Are you pessimistic or optimistic about man's future in this sense?

EISELEY: This is a question I've been asked many times and I always respond that I am an optimistic pessimist. There is no doubt that we live in a time of great crises, in terms of population explosion, the threat of starvation, a whole variety of things that we could list here. Parts of the world have fallen out of their old institutional adjustments to nature around them; they are swept increasingly into the whirlpool of western technology. Whether they survive and restructure societies in terms of that whirlpool or whether they sink within it, it is too early to tell. Of one thing I am very sure: it is not a thing that one can pass judgment upon in one generation, namely our own. It has been said that one should not equate one's own increasing senility with the fall of a civilization, and I try not to do that. On the other hand there are mounting problems—part of that great wave of which I spoke, an importunate towering wave which cannot be long delayed in its impact. And the question is whether, with all our technology, all our efforts, we can restructure, not alone in our own society but in societies of other parts of the world, important institutions which are now crumbling and eroding. A society without social institutions of some viability does not long survive. I know that when we are young we constantly tend to complain about how the elder generation doesn't respond rapidly enough to

the challenges in the environment—and, alas, this is sometimes
the case—but on the other hand, the student of social
institutions will tell you that there is a degree of necessary
rigidity in the important institutions of a society, or there is
social chaos. It's a little like building a skyscraper. It has to
have some rigidity to stand, but somewhere up there in the
upper reaches it also has to have "sway," and "sway" is just as
necessary to healthy institutions. Because of technological
innovations the rapidity of change in society is far greater than
ever before in human history. It's like a machine vibrating
at an increasingly fast pace. What was current for generations
before, to which man might slowly adjust, is changed. One
generation has far more difficulty in understanding its immediate
elders. And the situation here is one which mankind has
never equally experienced before. Human adaptability is being
stretched to the utmost. And since the situation is new, we
are faced with the inability to make analogies with what has
gone on in the past. For this reason, trying to be completely
scientific, I would not give up hope for man. I would only
say that his journey is beset with terrors.

MONTAGU: As Dr. Eiseley has pointed out, we are
living in a time of crisis, and I would suggest that the only
philosophically tenable position for even a pessimist in a time
of crisis is optimism—but not the old-style optimism which
defined the optimist as one who believes that this is best of all
possible worlds and the pessimist as one who is very much afraid
that the optimist is right. But rather I think the only practical
definition for an optimist in our own time is one who believes
that the future is uncertain. It will very definitely be certain if
we go on as we have been and do virtually nothing about it—
institutionalized as we have become, we have that chronic
disorder known as psychosclerosis, which inflicts itself upon
people of all ages, even very young ones, and which our so-called
educational systems are devised to engender.

On the other hand, as human beings in process of evolution,
I think that it is now more than ever necessary for each of us,
particularly those of us still living under some semblance of a
democracy, to realize that with freedom goes responsibility
and that it is the obligation, the moral obligation, of every

human being to make himself responsible for revaluating the things he has taken most for granted and to re-examine the institutions in which and under which he is living. I think this way we may have some chance of deriving a conclusion that will tell us what is right and what is wrong and what we, not the others, but what we need to do to set them right.

LARRABEE: What I confess I don't see in Dr. Eiseley's argument is how the road through these trackless troubles, how the responsible road, can be taken through the cloud of unknowing. I'm going to pursue you on your mysticism.

EISELEY: Go ahead.

LARRABEE: Let us define it—reaching for a definition something like what Aldous Huxley talks about in *The Perennial Philosophy*—as the belief, borrowing a term from science, in the divine ground, an "all" of some kind, which the human being can put himself in touch with if he is fortunate, or if certain conditions are fulfilled. This experience is a sudden opening up of the ordinarily narrow avenues of perception. Suddenly, instead of screening out the rest as we habitually do, leaving only a certain part of the wavelength of sight, only a certain number of possible sounds, only a certain number of possible ideas that may come through into our heads, suddenly the human psyche opens up and the totality gets through. This experience, it is assumed, replaces all others. It is indescribable; it is, once experienced, so much beyond anything else that the person to whom it happens thereafter believes in nothing else, or cares for nothing else. It has been described. Numbers of human beings have said that it happened to them. Where does that leave us? I confess, in the first place, not to being able to distinguish psychologically between this experience and many other hallucinatory experiences which have been described by people who were deprived of sense stimulation over a long period, or people who have been brainwashed, or people who have experienced religious conversion. Something can clearly happen to the human animal which is a shattering total experience of some kind, an involvement in the "all" which becomes very real for the person to whom it happens. But that it is a reliable way, one we can trust and follow, one through the immediate difficulties we face, this I confess I'm not convinced of.

EISELEY: Let me attempt very briefly to answer here. Perhaps because of some of my figures of speech Mr. Larrabee may have interpreted my point of view rather differently from what I intended.

First of all, I think we must remember that there is a difference between the life of the individual and the life of the society. Even so, the individual life and the societal one are intermixed and intermingled in the sense that what most of us believe will have a great deal to do with the way we operate in our particular social environment. Now, in quoting the unknown mystic who used the word "all," I did not mean to imply that to walk out into the street and suddenly have some blinding, shattering experience would necessarily point the road to the future or open the world in a totally new way. But I do believe that for each individual there is the possibility of salvation to the extent that he has self-knowledge which is not confined to science alone or to exterior things, but which includes certain of these other matters I mentioned: compassion, love, as Dr. Ashley Montagu has mentioned—some feeling for his fellows. I think that this in itself can be of benefit to our society at large, but over and beyond that, there is the reality. There is little use, in a way, of our talking abstractly about what our descendants may be doing a thousand years after we are gone. We may speculate, certainly—there is no harm in this— and we may hopefully speculate that the future contains something more than babies brought up in bottles. But each of us lives at his own point in time, and in that sense he is traveling his own road. This is what I'm trying basically to make clear; and it isn't necessary from this standpoint to be blinded by a shattering experience, although sometimes these things happen to people. Rather one's outlook can be compounded of right knowledge, right science, along with this other thing I was implying through the "all," that is, the knowledge not alone of exterior things, but the knowledge of the heart as well.

MAN AND THE FUTURE | 2

THE
CONTINUING SCIENTIFIC
REVOLUTION

Philip H. Abelson

As a graduate student, I was privileged to work with Ernest Lawrence and his cyclotron in the Radiation Laboratory at Berkeley. In 1938, no one in the laboratory would have predicted the advent of atomic energy. Nor would we have predicted more than a small number of other great developments that were to come. With such a lesson in mind, it is with considerable humility that I approach the great unknown of the future of man, and the topic of the continuing scientific revolution.

One of this nation's great men, who was also one of its great scientists, came close to an accurate forecast of the future. He was Benjamin Franklin. Franklin was aware of the potential role of science in human affairs. Here is a passage from a letter he wrote to Priestley in 1780: "The rapid progress true science now makes occasions my regretting sometimes that I was born too soon. It is impossible to imagine the height to which may be carried, in a thousand years, the power of man over matter. We may perhaps learn to deprive large masses of their gravity, and give them absolute levity, for the sake of easy transport. Agriculture may diminish its labor and double its produce;

all diseases may by sure means be prevented or cured, not excepting even that of old age, and our lives lengthened at pleasure even beyond the antediluvian standard. O that moral science were in as fair a way of improvement, that men would cease to be wolves to one another, and that human beings would at length learn what they improperly call humanity!"

Franklin was correct in many ways, especially in his dim view of the prospects of men's ceasing to be wolves. Even he, however, was conservative in his estimate of the tempo of the scientific revolution. Even he could not foresee the great change in man's status that has occurred.

A few hundred years ago man was little above the other animals. He was at the mercy of forces he did not understand and could not control. Today he is master of his destiny. He has the power to change his environment even on a planetary scale. To some extent, he can already control his own evolution. Not content with the vast powers at his disposal, he has harnessed science as an agent for further change. The weight of the resources of great nations is committed to speeding further innovations. Science has given man knowledge, and through technology that knowledge has been utilized to create unprecedented power and many options for action.

In attempting to look at the future of man, a number of factors cannot be evaluated. First, we cannot predict, except in general terms, the future course of science. Hence we cannot predict the new powers and options man will develop. The greatest imponderable, however, is man himself. Given tremendous power and countless options, what will he choose to do? Will he avoid nuclear war? Will he choose birth control or death control? Will population growth be checked, or will much of the planet be converted into an overcrowded slum?

I have mentioned only a few problems. Many more will arise. Man now has the knowledge and power to shape his future. He cannot escape from the need for decisions. Even the refusal to make judgments and take action is itself a decision. The future development of human affairs will be conducted in the framework of the options provided by science and technology. What can one say about the shape of these options? I will attempt to outline some of the future possibilities.

First, I will make some general remarks about the scientific revolution, which is not one revolution but many. There have been chemical, electronic, agricultural, medical, and energy revolutions.

We have been living through a period of unprecedented rate of change. People have become so accustomed to change that it is a common concept that science is unlimited in its capacity to create new knowledge. I disagree. I believe that a limited number of laws govern nature, and that most of them have been discovered. Major areas of potential knowledge—particularly in the physical sciences—have already been mined out. I do not wish to leave the impression that I believe no further advances in the physical sciences will occur. Rather I wish to indicate that in some fields there is only a limited potential for the creation of new revolutionary knowledge. As a simpe example, consider identification of isotopes of the elements. This was an active area in the 1920's and 1930's, but now nearly all the stable isotopes of the elements have been discovered. That work is completed for all time.

A further development in the mining-out process has occurred in recent years, namely a trend to more rapid exhaustion of the fundamental research potential of fields. It can be seen vividly in recent studies of the noble-gas compounds. Only a few years ago the first xenon fluorides were described. Since then more than a hundred papers have been published on the subject. Considering the detail in which the compounds have been studied, it seems that little more remains to be discovered about these chemicals with techniques now known.

John Platt has made the additional point that there are limitations on the changes that technology can bring. For instance, the big change in world-wide communication has already occurred. Once we can transmit sight and sound around the world within two seconds, there is little further to do but extend the networks. Consider speed of travel. We have made the leap from a walk to jet travel at 600 miles an hour, and experimental rocket planes have exceeded 4,000 miles per hour. John Platt asks, "How long can the acceleration of speed go on?" Then he remarks, "This is an easy question to answer, because it is finished. At around 100 miles an hour, we give up land transport and take to the air. At around 17,000 miles an hour, we give up air travel because we are in orbit. And this step is already behind us."

I turn now to sketch some of the probable future impact of energy and chemical revolutions. I believe that in these areas man has only a few options and consequently one can discuss the future with a good chance of coming close to actual developments.

The scientific basis for much of the energy revolution has been established. Nuclear fission, which was coupled to chain reaction in 1942, was a major step. It permitted use of uranium 235, which constitutes about 1 part in 140 of natural uranium. The next step, so-called breeding, will permit exploitation of most of the energy resident in all the uranium. Scientifically, this development is essentially complete; the major commercial power reactor groups are working out the technical details. Beyond fission is fusion; that is, tapping the potential energy of heavy hydrogen. This energy has been employed in the hydrogen bomb. Making it available for peaceful purposes, a major function of the Atomic Energy Commission's Sherwood program and the Plowshare program particularly, is progressing and will eventually succeed. The problems that remain in exploiting heavy hydrogen are of an engineering, rather than a scientific, nature. When the work is complete, the vast quantities of energy present in the heavy hydrogen of the oceans will constitute a reserve of energy a billion times as great as that of the fossil fuel reserves of the world.

The purely scientific aspects of the chemical revolution are surely considerably more than half complete. All the naturally occurring elements and many of their compounds have been studied intensively. As a result of work already accomplished, chemistry has won for itself a continuing, essential role in human affairs.

Almost all products that meet man's urgent needs involve chemistry. Food, clothing, shelter, medicine, transportation, and recreation depend on that science at every turn. Continuing research in chemistry itself will exploit opportunities created by new electronic instrumentation and by computers. Major large-scale, revolutionary, new information does not seem so likely. There will, nevertheless, be a multitude of advances that will increase the power of man to transform materials to meet his needs.

I will now discuss some of the implications of the energy and chemical revolutions and how they will, in important ways, shape man's future way of life.

In the United States, generation of electric power has been doubling every ten years. Use of other major forms of energy has been increasing also, though not so fast. Fuel reserves are not sufficient to meet our long-term needs. Even at present rates of consumption, conventional sources of petroleum within this country would be seriously depleted in another thirty years. Optimists talk of finding more oil, but the costs of doing so are increasing sharply. Within ten years, perhaps sooner, we will be using the oil shales of Colorado, Utah, and Wyoming for part of our hydro-carbons. The coal reserves, though great, are exhaustible; indeed, a recent government study of total United States fuel reserves indicated that we have only a thirty-year supply at current prices. More fuel is available, but it would cost more to extract it. In estimating such reserves, the standard unit is the so-called Q, which corresponds to the heat content of 40 billion (10^9) tons of high-grade coal. Current United States energy consumption is about 0.05 Q per year. The fuel reserve that can be obtained at present costs amounts to 1.5 Q. About 20 Q more can be obtained, but the cost, by present technology, would be multiplied fourfold. With the demand for energy continuing to increase, even the high-priced reserves would be largely exhausted within another hundred years. Prospects would be poor if a new energy source had not become available. Nuclear energy has now become competitive. Twenty years ago there was much talk about the wonders of the atomic age, and the public was led to expect sudden miracles. But the promise of competitive nuclear energy was steadily postponed; until three years ago, the promise seemed like a mirage.

In 1962, when a leading spokesman of the electrical industry estimated future costs of power, he stated flatly that nuclear power was not competitive with conventional energy. He estimated that in the period 1973-1978 nuclear power would cost between 6 and 7 mills per kilowatt-hour, while costs of conventional power would vary in the range 4 to 5 mills. That is, four short years ago a leading expert considered that even after fifteen more years nuclear power would not be competitive.

In two years the outlook had changed surprisingly. The General Electric Company entered into a contract to build a nuclear installation at Oyster Creek in New Jersey. This plant, to be completed in 1967-1968, is expected to deliver power at a cost below 4 mills per kilowatt-hour. In 1965, after the announcement of the contract for Oyster Creek plant, other utility companies contracted for eight major nuclear power plants. The competitive position of nuclear power is now excellent and is likely to get even better. New economies will come in part from a variety of improvements in design; a major further economy could come from larger installations.

The typical new plant has an installed capacity of about 600,000 kw. Weinberg and Young estimate that an 8,000,000-kw plant could be built producing power at 1.7 mills per kilowatt-hour. They also believe that further developments during the next sixty years will lead to nuclear power at 0.8 mill per kilowatt-hour, that is, at a cost of about one-fifth that of power derived from coal.

Nuclear energy plants have two other advantages. The first is that nuclear plant economics do not vary much with geographic location—a factor that gives many regions of this country and elsewhere better opportunities for industrial development. The second is that nuclear plants do not pollute the atmosphere with sulfur dioxide, nor do they release vast amounts of carbon dioxide. An excessive concentration of carbon dioxide might well change the earth's weather. This problem has been reviewed recently by Roger Revelle in a memorandum to the President's Science Advisory Committee. During the last century the amount of carbon dioxide in the atmosphere increased by 7 per cent. At present trends, the amount in the air will have increased

25 per cent by the year 2000. Accompanying this change would be an effect on the world's climate that cannot be estimated with precision, but it can be stated that the average temperature at the earth's surface could increase between 1° and 7° F. If half the fossil fuel reserves were consumed, this temperature increase could amount to as much as 20°. As a result, after some several hundreds of years, the polar ice caps would melt, sea level would rise about 300 feet, and many of the present major cities would be drowned.

Man is at present returning to the atmosphere and oceans, within a few centuries, the concentrated organic carbon accumulated in geologic formations during hundreds of millions of years. In doing so he will inevitably cause profound, unpredictable, and even lethal changes in his environment. The menace from carbon dioxide is distant, however, and most people find it convenient to ignore problems that need not be faced immediately. However we are already on the verge of an acute national problem affecting our environment: namely, air pollution.

Formerly, air pollution was a local problem, closely connected to industrial activity. Today, the principal source of pollution is the automobile. When motor vehicles burn fuel, they produce a number of products in addition to carbon dioxide and water. Significant amounts of carbon monoxide and nitrogen oxides are formed. At a concentration of slightly more than 1,000 ppm, carbon monoxide kills quickly. Most people experience dizziness, headache, and other symptoms at approximately 100 ppm. Concentrations approaching that value have been observed recently in most of the metropolitan centers.

In California, efforts have been made to decrease the amounts of carbon monoxide emitted by motor vehicles by means of devices such as catalytic afterburners. At the same time there has been a trend toward higher combustion-chamber temperatures. These efforts result in more complete combustion but also contribute to an increase in the production of oxides of nitrogen. Nitrogen dioxide is a poisonous brown gas. The threshold level for toxic effects is not well known, but it appears to be about 5 ppm. Concentrations approaching this have been observed in Los Angeles.

Thus far, people in other parts of the country have not suffered as much as the citizens of Los Angeles, but if present trends in pollution continue many of us will. During the autumn of the year temperature inversions in the atmosphere make much of the country subject to the hazard of heavy smog and even of dangerous pollution. These dangers and unpleasantness of air pollution will tend to hasten the implementation of the energy revolution. An increasing tempo of that revolution has been guaranteed on the economic grounds of cheaper power. The ultimate revolution itself is guaranteed, because the fossil fuels will become exhausted.

What will life be like when man can no longer utilize petroleum? What will man's energy requirements and options be a hundred years from now? What form will they take? My guess is that the nature of the energy sources will to a considerable degree shape the lives of people of the future. Today our lives and our communities are largely built around the automobile with its internal-combustion engine. What happens when fossil fuel becomes scarce and costly? Today most of our clothing is of synthetic fibers. We are using increasing amounts of plastics, detergents, paints, and a host of other chemicals, most of which are derived from natural gas, petroleum, or coal. What is to be done about home heating when fossil fuels become more costly or are exhausted?

One procedure would be to use nuclear energy as a means of re-creating the fossil fuels that we have been burning. That is, it would be possible, though costly, to make gasoline with carbon dioxide and water as starting materials. In principle, the present pattern of living might be preserved—automobiles, air pollution, and the rest. I believe, however, that the cities of the future will be molded by the economics of energy production and utilization.

With time and more experience, nuclear power plants will become reliable and prove safe. Their record so far is good. With time, public confidence in them will increase. Nuclear plants are clean and need give off no noxious fumes. They could be buried underground. There is no unsightly mess connected with them. In time, there would be little basis for banning nuclear reactors from metropolitan centers. They would supply central heating and energy for electricity, air conditioning, and preparation of food. Transportation, including small vehicles, would utilize electrical energy.

The availability of large amounts of cheap nuclear energy creates other potential patterns. One of them is large-scale conversion of salt water into fresh water. By applying currently reliable technology, the cost would be in the neighborhood of 22 cents per 1,000 gallons. Ultimately, the theoretical possibilities of membrane technology will be exploited, and costs could drop to a few cents per 1,000 gallons. Cheap fresh water will make the seacoasts more attractive and open up arid lands for use. More novel are the potentialities for colonization of the oceans. Some areas of the ocean, those near Hawaii, for instance, are very pleasant. Artificial floating islands with their nuclear power plants could be almost self-sufficient.

This country could easily feed much larger numbers than it now does, though perhaps not with conventional food. If the problem were only the supplying of man's material needs, a continuing increase in population could probably be cared for far into the future. Developments in nuclear technology promise the availability of almost unlimited amounts of energy. Utilizing such energy industrial chemists could convert plentiful raw materials such as water, air, and carbon dioxide into food, perhaps using microorganisms and animals as intermediates.

I believe that it would be technically feasible to feed and house in the United States a population 10 to 100 times as great as our present one. The problem, however, is not merely providing food and shelter. As the population grew, the contamination of the environment would also grow. Man would find it necessary to change or destroy nature further, in order to provide for the large masses of humanity. Science might find ways of dealing with the contamination of the environment so that the masses of people would not physically poison each other. But when humans are crowded together other kinds of effects are produced that may prove more difficult to deal with.

Man cannot live on energy alone. He requires also a variety of materials—metals, nonmetals, chemicals based on carbon. By applying present technology we are rapidly depleting our ores of many elements, and of others have never had our own supply. The geologists must find new sources of raw material, and over the long haul new points of view toward materials will come into being.

Cheap nuclear energy coupled with chemistry will permit exploitation of low-grade concentrations of minerals. At some time in the future, much of the whole crust of the earth will have been worked over to a depth of many miles. The ocean and its dissolved salts will be employed, and great new industries will exploit the vast resources of the ocean bottoms.

Of great possible economic significance are materials on the deep-sea floor. Among them are manganese nodules (nominally worth $45 to $100 a ton), which contain not only manganese but such other elements as copper, cobalt, nickel, molybdenum, vanadium, zinc, and zirconium. A recent report estimates total reserves of these nodules at a million million tons. To put a price on these reserves would be meaningless, but clearly a resource of fantastic magnitude is involved.

That the continental shelves are rich in oil, gas, and sulfur is well known. Moreover, potentially valuable mineral concentrations have received little attention, including placer deposits of drowned beaches. Diamond-bearing gravels off the coast of southwest Africa are an example, and recently substantial quantities of gold-bearing sands have been found in sea areas off Alaska. Tin ores have been found off Malaysia, and magnetite-rich sands are being mined near Japan.

Already major industrial organizations are quietly beginning to exploit the sea and the resources beneath it. The potential resources are tremendous. A scientific, technological, economic, political struggle for control of this wealth could be one of the major events of the next century.

The availability or scarcity of raw materials will influence the nature of future living patterns. Quite apart from scarcities, however, man will be forced into new attitudes and practices by the problems of pollution and waste management. Today there is increasing concern about these matters. Dean Athelstan Spilhaus of the University of Minnesota highlighted the problem recently when he wrote:

"Pollution increases not only because as people multiply the space available to each person becomes smaller, but also because the demands per person are continually increasing, so that each throws away more year by year. As the earth becomes more crowded, there is no longer an 'away.' One person's trash basket is another person's living space."

He writes further:

"Our whole economy is based on taking natural resources, converting them into things that are consumer products, selling them to the consumer, and then forgetting about them. But there are no consumers—only users. The user employs the product, sometimes changes it in form, but does not consume it—he just discards it. Discard creates residues that pollute at an increasing cost to the consumer and to his community."

The product of solid wastes has now reached eight pounds per person per day and is increasing. Many cities have exhausted their cheap sites for dumps and must haul refuse farther and farther away. The area required for sanitary landfilling is about one acre per year per 10,000 population when a 10-foot layer of waste is deposited. Unless policies change, the urban centers will soon become surrounded by mountains of waste.

One of these solutions to our waste-disposal problem is to reuse many of the materials instead of discarding them. Ultimately, civilization will find that it is cheaper to base an economy on reuse of materials; the alternate of obtaining costly raw materials and then being inundated by mounds of waste will not seem very sensible. Processes for reusing materials could easily be developed from existing knowledge.

In comparison with the energy and chemical revolution, the electronics revolution seems less complete. Potentials for scientific discovery remain, and exploitation of the technological potentialities is correspondingly less advanced and less knowable. The current focus of scientific efforts is research in solid-state physics. This activity has been a recognized branch of physics for only about twenty years, during which it has become the most active subfield in physics. A major milestone was the announcement of the transistor in 1948. Since then a host of new advances have been made, many of them opening up new areas of research with applications to other sciences and to technology. Masers and lasers provide powerful sources of light and promise new developments in communications. Recent discoveries in microelectronics provide very compact, very fast, circuits. I have recently been told of electronic components so small that four complete circuits could be hidden by the cross of cross hairs. These are only a sample of many new discoveries, and other findings are sure to come. Applications of the knowledge will have diverse important effects.

One important role of electronics, not generally appreciated, is the speeding of scientific advance through instrumentation. Furthermore, new instrumentation employed in the research laboratory today is used in the control laboratory and production plant tomorrow. The space effort would not be possible without the new compact circuits and special instrument packages. Solar batteries used in space will find application on the ground. Chemistry has become very dependent on new electronic devices; they had led to a renaissance in chemical research. In medical sciences there is wide use of microminiature solid-state temperature sensors, pressure transducers, and other acoustical devices. Such instruments will find greatly increased application in the automation of hospitals.

Electronic computers comprise one of the important areas for application of solid-state devices. The speed and capabilities of these machines are already very impressive, but new discoveries from solid-state physics will greatly improve both their speed and memory capacity. In turn, the computers will have, as they already have had, significant effects in speeding research in practically all lines of science.

They are especially valuable in high-energy physics, space research, geophysics, crystallography, medical studies, and in the behavioral sciences.

Up to the present, research workers have employed standard models of computers for their work and have designed their research to fit the capabilities of the machines. Ultimately, the needs of various branches of science may lead to computers designed for maximum effectiveness in specific applications. This could be an extremely important development. Some people believe that further developments in mathematics could change methods of presenting problems to computers, rendering the machines more effective in handling many scientific questions.

Even though only a small part of its potential users or usefulness has yet been realized, already the computer has added greatly to our capabilities. Some of the accomplishments are described in a recent report entitled "Digital Computer Needs in Universities and Colleges." One interesting statistic from that report is that the combined calculating capacity of these machines in the United States is more than ten times as great as the combined calculating capacity of its inhabitants. The machine has already got us outnumbered by ten to one.

The most advanced computers can perform numerical calculations at least a million times as fast as a human being. Not only can the computer do what a million persons can do, but the concentration of power makes feats possible that the million humans could never combine their efforts to achieve. A striking example is the launching of artificial satellites and space vehicles generally. To aim the booster from the launching pad with the accuracy required to put the satellite into the proper orbit would be impossible. But even while the booster is still burning, radars determine its position and velocity, and a computer has enough speed to determine the uncorrected orbit of the satellite and to specify the necessary corrections in time to have them made before the booster has finished firing. There is no way in which a million, or even a billion, humans working simultaneously with paper and pencil could match this accomplishment.

This example is illustrative of a class of applications of the computers. Through electronics it is possible to make almost instantaneous measurements on many systems. The resultant data can be fed to a computer that provides an almost instantaneous response. The total system can act with speeds far beyond any human capability.

Another important class of problems involves the analysis of enormous quantities of data. The computer can assimilate and store far more data than any human can. It can also be programmed to ask a host of detailed questions about correlations among the items. Exploitation of these capabilities will enable man to explore problems too complex for unaided human minds.

Applications of this type have already occurred. The successful development of jet aircraft was heavily dependent upon computers, and it's been said that the development of those aircraft would not have occurred had not computers been available.

But the computer is not a magical device that can do everything. Efforts to translate from Russian to English by means of it have not proved rewarding. I have talked to some of the scientists who have tried to use the broken English that comes out of the machine translation and they find it takes them about four times as long to decipher the broken English as it does an expert to translate Russian in the first place. The use of computers in the storage and retrieval of information will undoubtedly be important; however, the information retrieved is no better than what goes into the machine: that is, garbage in, garbage out.

A potential development that should concern us all is the power the computer gives centralized government. The use of computers by the Internal Revenue Service will make honest people out of most of us, but it is simultaneously a big step toward control of a population by a dictator. In principle, the capability right now exists to monitor all telephone calls. Roger Revelle has asked what will happen to the citizen when his identity and every detail of his life are coded and classified in the government's computing system. At present the fallibility of government is the safeguard of the citizen. What happens when the government becomes infallible because it is operated by a computing machine?

In the physical sciences a pattern has been discernible in the relation of scientific research, technology, power, and options for mankind. Research creates knowledge; applications of the knowledge to human needs followed. The pattern was not without exceptions, but it has been a major feature of science particularly of the last generation. In biology this relation has not been so clear-cut. Sometimes practical applications followed research, as in genetics; sometimes research was stimulated by an empirically derived practical application. Thus vaccination was practiced long before viruses had been isolated. Antibiotics had conquered many diseases before we understood much about their detailed mechanisms of action.

Major portions of the scientific revolution in biology have already occurred. They have had great practical consequences. A combination of biological discoveries and utilizations of chemistry and machinery has revolutionized agriculture. Biochemistry has provided a scientific basis for nutrition. Microbiology has provided the key to a greatly increased life expectancy.

In recent years the methods and techniques of the physical sciences have been increasingly utilized in research in the biological sciences. The resultant new knowledge is tending to lead rather than to follow practical applications.

We cannot say what the nature of the new knowledge will be, or how it will be applied. We can only make some very general observations. First, a substantial fraction of the best minds of our nation are now occupied with biological research. At the moment, many are heavily engaged in studies of the mechanisms of genetics. Others are seeking to elucidate the processes by which the fertilized egg develops to the fetus and then to the infant. Still others are inquiring into all aspects of the operation of the human mind. From this continuing research will come knowledge, applications, power, and options. I will not attempt to predict either the knowledge or its consequences, but they will be substantial. I will merely touch on one example. Knowledge of genetics is evolving rapidly. The basis of inheritance and the mechanisms by which the genetic code is transcribed are fairly well understood. Progress in studies of microorganisms has been especially fast. It is possible to alter the genetic makeup of bacteria in an increasing number of precise ways. Eventually many applications of biological engineering to microorganisms will be made. Although controlled laboratory change of human genetic DNA seems at the moment some distance away, the quality of the research talent makes further dramatic advances inevitable. Two applications have been described as being almost feasible. One is control of the sex ratio in humans. The second is the production of parthenogenetic offspring.

The new knowledge would extend man's power in the practical use of genetics to improve or to change livestock and other animals. Man already has options in guiding his evolution. They are not new, and their possibilities were discussed some years ago. Recently, some geneticists, especially H. J. Muller, have renewed their advocacy of deliberate efforts to improve the human stock. Julian Huxley has pointed out that an increase in the average I.Q. of 1.5 per cent would lead to a doubling of the number of persons having an I.Q. of 160 or more. Muller would achieve improvements by voluntarily conducted germinal choice. He advocates establishment of sperm banks and preservation of semen much as is done with cattle. Professor Muller has made few converts. Rather, he has awakened opposition among many scientists.

One feature of knowledge and its attendant power is its two-edged characteristic. The fire that warms the hearth can consume the house. Nuclear energy, which provides the prospect of long-term benefits, is accompanied by a continuing potential for savage destruction. The computer providing automation brings potentials of unemployment and tight government control. Even the medical revolution, which has saved many lives and spared much suffering, has another side. With an increase in life expectancy from thirty to seventy has come a population explosion. In the future, man's ingenuity and character will be strained as he attempts to reap the constructive aspects of science while avoiding the pitfalls it creates.

A sharp test of man's flexibility is now in progress in the population explosion. The problem does not seem acute in the advanced countries. Citizens of these nations are relatively well educated and many are already responding. Recent figures released for the United States showed that population growth was at its lowest rate in about fifteen years. Part of the problem remains, but we have time and the facilities to solve it. In more than half the world the problem is acute, and perhaps it will not be solved. Professor Raymond Ewell, Vice President for research at the State

University of New York at Buffalo, believes that the world is running short of food. In recent congressional testimony he said:

". . . the general picture is that since 1960 agricultural production in Asia, Africa, and Latin America has been growing at rates of around 1 per cent to 2 per cent per year while populations have been growing at 2.5 per cent to 3 per cent per year. This means that the per capita production of food has been declining at 1 per cent to as much as 2 per cent per year.

"If these trends continue for the next ten to fifteen years, mass starvation will result."

Then he says, "The political and economic consequences of widespread famine in Asia, Africa, and Latin America are certain to be massive and far-reaching. *It seems unlikely that stable governments can be maintained in countries where a large part of the population is starving.*"

Professor Ewell is most urgently concerned about India. India has long been recognized as the country most vulnerable to famine. The recent record drought has been particularly damaging. There have been food riots in some parts of India, and Dr. Ewell suggests that quite possibly a million people may die of starvation before the drought is alleviated.

If massive U.S. aid is effective on this occasion, will India take the necessary steps to bring food and population into balance? Or will our aid merely guarantee a greater catastrophe later on?

Quite apart from our humanitarian instincts, we have an important stake in this question. The overthrow of stable governments, coupled with a Communist take-over, would be profoundly disturbing. If this nation is concerned about developments in Vietnam, what would its response be to Russian or Chinese domination of India or a series of Communist revolutions throughout Latin America?

The impending crisis can be met, but a long-term solution cannot take the form of ever-increasing aid from us in the form of food. The underdeveloped nations must develop the capacity to solve their own problems. Birth control is a possible partial solution. But the real solution is to master the scientific revolution and to use constructively and responsibly the options that science has created.

I have surveyed some of the options created by science and technology and have indicated areas in which further developments are likely to occur. I have outlined a few of the decisions that man is already facing. He will face more, for his capability of controlling nature and the environment will increase.

But the coin of power has another side, responsibility. The future of man is under the control of man and will be determined by the wisdom and restraint with which he exercises his new powers.

We are privileged to be living at a unique time to witness an event that has never happened before and will not happen on earth again. Julian Huxley described this special moment eloquently when he said, "The evolution of this planet as a unit in the cosmic process has been going on for perhaps 5,000 million years. Life was evolved here after about half of this huge span of time, and has itself been evolving during the later half of the period. . . . We, like all other organisms and all other features of the earth, are products of this process of evolution. We men belong to the latest dominant type to be produced, and are now responsible for the future evolution of the planet. . . . We are privileged to be living at a crucial moment in the cosmic story, the moment when the vast evolutionary process, in the small person of enquiring man, is becoming conscious of itself."

COMMENTARIES

BOWMAN: This brilliantly comprehensive paper of Dr. Abelson's gives us a great many things to think about and I hesitate to bring it down to details, but perhaps that's the best way to discuss it.

As the only engineer among these eminent scientists here I feel I have a little in common with a couple of cows that were standing in a pasture in Kansas. A truck went by, carrying a sign on its side that read "Abbott's Milk—Homogenized, Pasteurized, Irradiated, Vitamin C Added." One cow looked at the other and said, "It makes one feel pretty inadequate, doesn't it?" Engineers sometimes have a feeling of inadequacy in the face of this great scientific revolution whose prolific production of scientific information is not being adequately utilized. This is a problem for both scientists and engineers, I think, because it concerns their ability to carry on scientific research, and because more money is available for scientific research than for engineering research. I've never figured out just why this is so, except that science can be talked about as "pure" science. Nothing about engineering is pure in this sense—it's commercial—so that it doesn't command as much research money.

In this connection it was most interesting to hear Dr. Abelson state that 70 per cent of the problems we will face in the next century will be engineering problems. And our real problem, both engineers and scientists, is to be aware of existing knowledge and to learn how to store and retrieve the information which is being produced in such prolific amounts, so that we can compare research and give priority to the type of research that we need. We may know a lot more than we need to know about a great many things, but until we are able to find out what we have learned, this seems to me to be one of the real problems of our scientific revolution: to have an inventory of what we have and then to go ahead.

LARRABEE: Can I say I don't agree? I've been trying to decide whether I disagreed with 35 per cent of what Dr. Abelson said or 55 per cent or 75 per cent. Much as my heart warmed to his final paragraph, I think it would be better if I said I disagreed with everything he said, because then we would have a more clear-cut difference of opinion.

The difference is one of spirit. It's a difference in what is meant by innovation; it's a difference in interpretating the relationship between science and technology; it's a difference—inevitably, I fear—in a definition of science itself. I am put off by little quite so much as the phrase, coming from a scientist, that something is "fairly well understood." It is a statement frequently made. It was made back in the early days, at the birth of modern science, by both Bacon and Descartes, the founding fathers, each of whom said that if his method was truly and well applied, all of the problems of physical nature would be solved in a limited number of years. One of them gave six years and the other gave sixty.

The perennial statement on the part of science that there are no more discoveries to be made—or in Dr. Abelson's words, "I believe that there are a limited number of laws governing nature and that most of them have been discovered"—is its perennial pratfall. Year after year, generation after generation, it happens, and one needs only to take the examples that Dr. Abelson himself gave. He opened with a lovely description of what it was like to be with Ernest Lawrence at Berkeley and the cyclotron in the early days. He went on to speak of the noble-gas compounds. I'm sure you could have found dozens of chemists who would have said that the noble gases were "fairly well understood," before the breakthrough which produced a hundred papers, as he said, showing that they weren't fairly well understood. The stellar distances were "fairly well understood" until Harlow Shapley completely changed them.

Science is something very different from this, and to suppose that its future is conditioned by the position it is in now seems to me, if I may say so as an outsider, completely contrary to the spirit of science, and I hate to see scientists indulge in it.

To forecast a nightmare on the basis of what science has to say about many of the problems of the present day involves me in another disagreement, and that is a disagreement with the proposition that if you have described the scientific parameters of a problem you have described the problem. This is so obviously not true that it seems almost impolite to say it, particularly when the various dimensions have been so elegantly, so clearly, and so truthfully described by Dr. Abelson. But he has described only the scientific boundaries. What he says of the fossil fuels is certainly true, but it sets aside the question of where use of the fossil fuels came from, and how we got ourselves involved in using petroleum. The automobile is a villain for many others besides scientists, and many of us besides scientists have been fighting against it on many of the fronts on which it devastates our lives. His words about the pollution of our environment could be extended even further in other dimensions, in the dimension of what this gadget has done to our cities, what it has done to the quality of our lives, and so on. And to do the subject justice one would have to speak of these, one would have to say something of the human motivations which lie behind them, why all of us can come into an auditorium like this and freely cuss the automobile and say how it ruins us all and then happily go out and get in automobiles and drive away.

How to disentangle ourselves from our sins of pride is a question which has only begun to affect the scientists. They have begun to realize that the question is there. They have begun to realize that the desire to master nature is like the desire to sharpen only one blade of a sword; the sword has begun to cut both ways. And for that reason it is a welcome relief when one finds a scientist who treats science as something else than a device for saying that all the rest of us are foolish, or that once the scientific side of the problem is clear all that remains is for the rest of us to put it to work. I cannot agree that it is a matter merely of informing the public about the science of the matter; I think that plainly is not the case, and I say so in what I take to be the spirit of Dr. Abelson's peroration.

ABELSON: I knew of the past history of unsuccessful predictions with respect to the future of science when I prepared my talk. However, such precedents are not necessarily applicable now. There have been changes since Bacon and there have been changes since the beginning of this century when some distinguished prophets went awry. Today a vast army of scientists is actively engaged in research. Sixty years ago science was largely an amateur sport; today it is one of the driving, motivating features of great nations. Tremendous sums of money are being spent on it. How much did the government spend on science sixty years ago? Peanuts.

SHAPLEY: Mr. Chairman, I'd like to report myself as agreeing very largely with what Mr. Abelson had to say and disagreeing very largely with the things that Mr. Larrabee didn't say, but implied. You mentioned, both of you did, about evolution being a part of the picture and I thought I might be informative, not argumentative, to point out how this evolution business has been going of late.

You'll remember that a good many years ago we boldly thought of evolution as being only biological—botanical and animal, that was all of evolution. Some few talked about the evolution of societies. But now it's gone much further. We've found strong evidences—not always proofs, because generally we don't get proofs, we get high probabilities, that stars evolve. We don't stick around to see them evolve but we have the machinery that "watches" them and we agree on this evolution of stars. We go beyond stars and find there is very good evidence of evolutionary trends among the galaxies. We can study a planet like the earth or the earth-moon system, and there have been changes over not too many years, so again we find evolutionary progress. But the great one to me in importance is the increasing evidence that matter itself evolves, that the atoms of which you are composed all have evolved from other atomic forms. We have several gaps to fill but we have made very great progress. So the conclusion I want to point out is that every process you can mention or think about is a process of evolution. There is a cosmic evolution that runs all the way through the universe. It's pleasant to be a part of such evolving. For instance, I'm going to evolve now by passing this on to somebody else.

FULLER: I've found the experience of listening to Dr. Abelson one of the kind I like to have once in a while, a kind of shower bath. It makes me really want to go to work.

I thought of one or two items it might be worth noting during this centennial meeting of well-informed human beings in order possibly to come to some new realization of thought.

One of the things that came to mind as Dr. Abelson spoke about fossil fuels and the cost of generation of atomic energy was the fact that I find society completely passive in accepting statements about costs; the cost of the generation of electricity from atomic power is compared to the cost, as was said, of producing power in another manner, as, in this example, the burning of fossil fuels. But included in the estimate I found no cost accounting of the price of putting those fossil fuels down into the earth. Just how were these resources captured on earth? What would it cost to replace these capital wealth energy sources? I think it fantastic with what irresponsibility we talk about costs.

I believe that New York City has started to run out of water. We shall run out of water in many places, but at the present moment there are already two or three very critical spots. Then we begin to talk about desalinization. Then the costs are given for that as against what it costs to just put some pipes from the lakes up in the hills and run the water down, letting the gravity pull it down to the city to be polluted and dumped into the sea. Nobody says, "What did it cost to get the water up that hill?" I've been a sailor, and we've had desalinization in the Navy for over a half a century. The question there was posed differently: what was the cost if you didn't have desalinization? The answer was: no navy to run the world.

The stakes are very high: when we run out of water it's going to take three or four years to get other ways of producing water. And man won't have time when he's busy dying. I don't think our public statements on cost are intelligent or comprehensive enough to give us adequate guidance.

I also find completely wrong the concept of competition as being adequate to solve this nation's problems. For example, I've taken photographs in Los Angeles of the smog as it comes over the city. Every Christmas week in Los Angeles the smog disappears; it goes away because the industrial plants, particularly the refineries to the southwest of Los Angeles, are shut down for the holidays. It's just as clear as can be. After New Year's comes an industrial day and I've photographed that big brown cloud coming north again over the city. There's no question about what that enveloping blanket is. Mist is formed on the western shores of all the islands on the Pacific and on the great western shores of America because of temperature differentials and mist sustaining electrical differentials. These mists would ordinarily be diffused in due course by the wind, but when they become laden with industrial fumes, their heavier densities make them come down and capture other even lower gases such as fumes from automobiles. But the hard fact is that city governments have to meet payrolls and those payrolls are paid from the city's tax base. Since industry pays much of those taxes, the government fought very hard to get those industries, and they aren't going to say to those industries, "You have to take care of those fumes, you will have to precipitate them and so forth." Industries say, "We cannot compete with other industries who are not operating under the same geographic conditions. If we have to precipitate our fumes, we will not be able to stay in your city and put our money in your tax base." So the politicians in Los Angeles try to find some other cause for the smog situation besides industry. The politicians used to say, "Well, it's because the people incinerate; so it's really your fault, people." The people stopped incinerating, but the smog is still there. So now the government says, "People, it's your cars that are fuming, so it's entirely your fault." And I have to say that this is simply not true. People were using their cars more than ever during Christmas week and there was no smog. I've been taking these pictures for fifteen years, and the purer air condition exists just for that week from Christmas to New Year's day.

I'd like to suggest here in our meeting there is much to be

considered that relates to how man effectively does take the initiative to determine whether he is going to be a success or not a
success. All this information is utterly useless unless it is turned to
man's account as to how he can be successful on earth. Hearing
the discussion of burning up all the fossil fuels within another
generation, I think about the fundamental morality of our
society today in thinking that it's all right to say to the generation
to come, "Darlings, you'll be the ones to get it so that we
could make a profit this year." And I don't really believe that
talking this way makes me a Communist. I notice that the
Communists are also burning up fossil fuels. I find them equally
immoral in burning up their bank account. When we talked
about comparative costs in using fossil fuels, I said that the cost
of putting them in the ground, of their original creation, should
be included; but the idea of digging them out is also like saying,
"How much does it cost to blast our way into the safe to take
out the money?" Is that a good way of figuring costs?

Man on earth has been behaving very unwisely. He discovered atomic energy just in time to overlap his exhaustion of
the fossil fuels, but he still hasn't learned to think in terms of
the conservation of energy. Man does not yet conduct himself
on that basis: he has deliberately taken out those energy savings
that have been concentrated in fossil fuels and has detonated
them and sent them off as dissociative energies back into
universe. It is possible that such action may have prematurely
used an energy storage essential to spring earth into some kind
of universe—balancing, energy-detonating function some day.
Or, assume that man in the interim could learn to locally aid the
inhibition of energies which he might need to give him the
necessary capability to even get off the planet before his energy-
stored earth became a new radiant source.

Man is certainly using very short-term reasoning. He has
not used any long-term logic about man's life on earth, and
never thought about his grandchildren or great grandchildren or
the children of a thousand years hence. It seems much less
expensive to take energy savings out of the earth than it is to
take the trouble to harness the enormous daily income energies
from the winds, tides, sun, and other sources. Of course, it is
easier to rob the bank than it is to do new work—at least while
there is still money in the bank. This is the kind of argument

that mankind is employing. The same reasoning has been underwriting the validity of all his economics and what we call enterprise.

The earth's surface receives energy from three main inputs: one, radiant solar energy; two, the kinetic and potential energy of the earth in the gravitational system; and three, geothermal energy from the earth's interior. Other energy sources are sub-cycles of these, e.g., the fossil fuels are stored solar energy deposits while water power taps the local hydrological cycles and wind power, the atmospheric circulations. The fossil fuel "capital" energies are, of course, exhaustible. The other two examples are "income" energies with daily regenerative cycles. I went to a little valley high up on the Greek island of Rhodes last year. It is an extraordinary place where there were once ten thousand windmills. In an older age, man did very well with his daily energy income by using the wind not only with windmills, but also with sailing ships that took him around the world. Ancient man did not exhaust the capital energies of the earth. Today, man has lost some of these quite beautiful wind arts, but with our great knowledge of aerodynamics it now seems possible to build some very extraordinary energy-impounding machines employing the wind.

The head of the United States Navy's Bureau of Weapons' Design Activities points out that of all the sources of energy operative around the world there is none so plentiful as wind power. In contrast to sun power which is available only when we are on the sunny side of the earth, winds are available all around the earth over both land and sea. The only unfavorable thing about the winds has been their intermittency. Their magnitudes, when operative, are very great, and man could do his work very well with them if ways could be found of handling and storing the energies. Man is learning to do this quite well.

The prospect of future energy sources does, in the main, belie most local resource estimates. Much work is already in hand and great progress made in the use of solar power converters. Electric power generation development from geothermal heat has been underway for some time in various areas. Nuclear power plant development has already widened its scope in terms of multi-national cooperative exploration and use, as for example "Euratom." It will possibly soon become one of our main energy transformations. Relative to this development is, of course, the now largely latent capacities of the oceans for providing enormous fuel sources. Controlled thermonuclear reactors using deuterium or heavy hydrogen as their main source of transformative material have been under experiment since 1945. One part of this hydrogen isotope is available in every six thousand parts of sea water. At present ocean volumes, it has been estimated that there is enough deuterium in the sea to generate a thousand times more energy for the next million years than is generated in the world today. The above list by no means exhausts the possibilities in the present of extending the range of technical developments in energy conversion advantages. Certain of the most recent technical advances, such as the "fuel cell," afford higher energy conversion efficiency—in this case 80 per cent—than many of our present "engines."

Tidal power is already harnessed in various parts of the world and rivaled by other potential inland water power sources as yet untouched. At Passamaquoddy, for instance, there are tremendous eighteen-foot tides twice a day. The fantastic magnitude of the water weight pulled out and towards the earth eighteen feet twice daily is far mightier than any tide man has as yet harnessed. It was said politically that the energy advantage at Passamaquoddy was unusable because the energies so harnessed could not be transmitted far enough from their source to reach any industrial center. Thus the project was dropped.

The history of increase in voltages, distances, and volumes of electrical energy transmission has been tied directly to the progressive limits of practically manufacturable, installable, and maintainable equipment that could be realized from the comprehensive conversions of pure science into objective-use technologies, as also modified by the physical resources becoming progressively available to industrial use. Generally speaking, the higher the voltage, the greater both the volumes at which and the distances to which electrical energy can be transmitted. By the use of transformers, electric energy generated at safely workable low voltages may be stepped-up to high voltage levels for transmission, and again stepped-down at the receiving end for safe domestic and industrial use.

High voltage conductance—heretofore primarily at 138,000

kilo volts and at 230,000 kilo volts—has represented the
maximum level of high voltage transmission feasibility of the
last two decades. The transmission distance theoretically permitted by the highest of these voltages was, in 1936, 1,400
miles. But due to fluorescent line losses, the practically profitable
distance was only 340 miles. Hoover Dam to Los Angeles
was a typically practical limit. Today, however, technological
improvements are now permitting transmission voltage step-ups
of importantly improved magnitude: to 380,000, to 500,000
and to 1,000,000 kilo volts or one billion volts. This new era
of power transmission is spoken of in the electrical industry as
"U.H.V.," ultra-high-voltage transmission. Through U.H.V.,
we are going to be able to send energy 1,500 miles. Far remote
spots of great energy income such as Passamaquoddy can now
be hooked up to areas where man has high civilization needs.
Africa and China could be the world's main energy producing
and transmitting sources within a not-too-distant future.

The next thing I would like to do is to speak rudely about
the world of professional engineering, professional architecture,
and professional science. These professions are slave professions.
There have been approximately no changes in the socio-economic
relationships of engineers and architects since those in Egypt
five thousand years ago. The engineer and the architect perform
their arts only when a client puts them to work. Though seemingly freed today from slavery, they are retained at a money
price by clients. This is to say they are financially enslaved and
committed to carrying out the clients' design concepts. This
is also to say that they do so in order to be able to live. This
is no different, as far as fundamentals go, from being commanded
by the Pharaoh to realize and detail his prime pyramidal or
columnar concepts with death the alternative.

I have heard scientists and engineers speak about what
society ought to do or what the scientists and engineers ought
to do about modern problems, but there is nothing they can do
to realize advanced design solutions under the terms of the
present economic authority of the client wherein the professional
designers can only go to work when they are employed. The
client says to the architect and the engineer, "I am going to
expend so much capital to take the fossil fuel out of the earth
and to build a factory here and an office building there and I'm

going to manufacture this and that. You work out the structural and mechanical details and report back to me." Businessmen or politicians hold the grand strategy initiative. Whether it is for the good of future generations to exhaust earth's fossil fuels does not come within the scope of decision open to the engineers, scientists, and architects. Whether most effective education for humans consists in a complex of buildings, a hired staff hustling for tenure, and a syllabus does not come within the purview of the scientist, engineer, or architect.

I think that I would be remiss in not giving you my vigorous feelings about the complete inefficiency of our assuming that the politicians are going to be good strategists on how to employ our resources. The condition of science today as the servant of politicians is deplorable. To say how else society should be articulated is a great challenge, and that is a challenge at which we must begin to look as we come out of this meeting. I don't see this challenge being met by politicians in Russia or in China. I don't think it can be met by politicians. I don't need any politician in my family to make things run. Personally, I'm quite confident that if we begin to deal with our problems in the proper manner, world society will behave very well.

One of the other things Dr. Abelson mentioned was the possibility of the biological development of genetic design alterations and improvements in the human brain as related to the way we cope with problems. Dr. Abelson mentioned the words "behavioral sciences" but went no further. Some of you know about the behavioral sciences today and their relation to the environment. Dr. Shapley spoke about what Professor C. H. Waddington, geneticist at the University of Edinburgh, has named the "epigenetic landscape." In the epigenetic landscape man and other life alter the landscape and thereby alter them-selves. There is a continual evolutionary development in the interplay of all the patterns of the universe—even those things we used to call inanimate are interactive. Life alters the land-scape, then the landscape alters life—the inanimate winds and waters alter the land and vice versa. Neither the individual species of life nor the physical components of the inanimate chemistry of the environment, nor the whole, synergetic landscape ever return exactly to their respective previous conditions. Entropy and evolution are inherent. The inanimate physical complexes become increasingly and superficially random while the biological phenomena regenerate with increasing orderliness of species and sub-species regularities.

There is also a definite relationship between the environmnt and man's I.Q. Experiments show that the environment plays an important part in whether man's brain as originally inventoried comes into use during life. The brain has extraordinary capabilities, and these various coordinated capabilities come into play following special sequential schedules unique to each individual. Put your finger in the palm of a newborn baby's hand and the baby will close its tiny hand deftly around your finger. If you try to withdraw your finger, the baby's hand responds instantly to the withdrawal tension and opens its hand. Its tactile apprehending organism is apparently operative in superb coordination at birth. Days later, the pre-set chromosomic "alarm clock" in the brain of the baby calls the hearing function into operation. Days later, the baby sees for the first time. One by one the brain's alarm clocks and the chromosome ticker-tape instructions inaugurate use of the child's vast inventory of intercoordinate capabilities and faculties. The child is not in fact taught and cannot be taught by others to inaugurate any of these capabilities. He teaches himself—if given the chance at the right time. If these capabilities are not properly greeted by the environment—and by environment I include people as well as inanimate elements—one capability after another will get pinched off and become inoperative.

Dr. Benjamin Bloom, in his book *Stability and Change in Human Characteristics*, has shown that if you can give him the data regarding environmental conditions for an individual from the time of birth up to and including seventeen years, he will be able to determine that individual's I.Q. at seventeen. Dr. Bloom's I.Q. predictions over a very large sample have been accurate to within one point of the real value I.Q.'s, thus showing irrefutably that I.Q. is a consequence of the environment. Therefore, I'm not interested in Dr. Abelson's genetic redesign of the brain to improve man's original inventory, which I think is far beyond present realizations of his enormous potential. Instead I am both interested and ever more actively engaged in allowing man to improve his position through environmental reform that can permit him to become the success to which he is born.

ABELSON: I'm not in favor of crash programs to improve the genetic stock of man. We should be conservative in areas having to do with human evolution. We have been millions of years getting where we are and I cannot see the necessity or wisdom of a crash program to improve man. We should understand our limitations and objectives better before we exercise some of the options. Nevertheless, it is well to be aware of the powers that are at hand and the areas in which decisions of one kind or another will eventually be made.

BLAKESLEE: It's very apparent that this rapid rate of change is doing powerful things to us human beings, some of them to us, some of them for us, some even against us. It is a diet of change that is very rich and sort of giddy and it's being force fed; it's challenging our habits, our prejudices, our attitudes, even our desires and hopes, and straining our institutions which can become rigid or get hardening of the arteries just as well as human beings do. We know too, as was pointed out, that changes bring brand-new problems in continuous harvest. I wonder whether it might not be useful to think of the results of these changes in terms of indigestion, a kind of social indigestion, and then to think that what we need are more "social inventions," not more physical inventions, but social inventions and innovations actively sought to solve social problems.

So I have two questions: One is, do you think the social sciences are being a bit neglected or undersupported relative to the physical and biological sciences? Could more research and more support for research in these fields—psychology, sociology, psycho-biology, and the like—offer us more chances of solving some of these problems which are the result of our scientific revolution? And the second question is, would it be desirable to get more of the public, the ordinary citizens, involved in seeking these social inventions? As I understand it, the patent office has been one of the bulwarks of our technological progress; any citizen may have an idea and if he can prove that it is original and that it works, he gets protection, he gets a reward really. Would there be some sense, then, in setting up a sort of Office of Social Inventions, whether in a community, federal, or state government, to encourage a flow of ideas and experiences from average citizens to help resolve some of these problems that we now face or will face in the future, ideas that would allow us to live with and cope with the scientific revolution without losing our individuality and our humanness?

ABELSON: I will respond to the second question first. I think that a major part of achieving a solution to almost any problem is to recognize that the problem exists. There is something about the challenge of a widely known problem that leads humans to respond imaginatively. The fact that ordinary citizens are interested in a problem will cause some of the best minds of the nation to address themselves to it. We are in need of further development of our ethics and philosophy. This is not my field, but it seems to me that much of our Christian ethics—which are generally admirable—were developed at a time when certain different realities existed. A few generations ago many of the things that happened to man seemed to be the will of God; but in the future most of the things that are going to be happening to man are not going to be the will of God, they are going to be the will of man. Some further adjustment in ethics must correspondingly be made.

As to your first question about support of social sciences, there is a questionable unanimity in Washington and elsewhere that the social sciences have been undersupported and that to solve social problems we must pour more money into the social sciences. I would be much more confident about what might come out of more support if I could see some definite progress or if I could see some new creative ideas coming out of social sciences.

CLARKE: Well, I don't want to say too much now because I'm afraid I might shoot off all my ammunition before Wednesday evening. I'll only make a few points.

You mentioned that some of the ideas of the Christian attitude are based on situations no longer valid. I was thinking of the old Biblical injunction, "Be fruitful and multiply," which you now have to turn into, "Be fruitless and divide." We have been discussing many of the things that we've been doing with our world and it does seem that our attitude toward industry and mankind as a whole, toward some of the problems which we are passing on to the future generation, is why should we bother about posterity; what has posterity ever done for us? For instance, you were talking about nuclear power stations. What about the gigantic quantities of radioactive waste which we are going to accumulate unless we ship them off into space and even that may cause traffic problems eventually? That is going to limit the production of power by fission processes; I rather suspect that fission is going to be a dead end anyway after we put a few hundred billion dollars into it, and for this reason, if no other, fusion will have to take over. Going from the sublime to the ridiculous, another hazard which I worry about is the amount of indestructible plastic wrapping material we are using; sometimes when I'm wrestling with food containers I think of the ultimate fate of the human race: are we to die of starvation as muscles atrophy and as plastic containers become more and more impenetrable?

Finally, another ominous possibility I would like to leave with you just before you go to sleep, and I hope it will generate some nightmares—I know for a fact that one young American Nobel Prize winner is convinced that the greatest crime wave in history is going to hit the world, probably in less than a decade, as the result of the perfection of organ transplantation. If you stop to think you will see exactly what he's worried about, because there just won't be enough organs to go around.

ABELSON: I don't find much to disagree with in Mr. Clarke's remarks. However, I would remind you that radioactive wastes can be contained and that the radioactivity decays. That is not the case with CO_2. It takes a long time for CO_2 to be absorbed in the ocean.

MAN AND THE FUTURE | 3

AN APPEAL TO REASON

Charles E. Whittaker

It seems clear that most of our people have now come to understand that we are all involved in unusual ferment, and many of us are confused and bewildered. Many are asking the reasons for this, what it means, and where it leads and ends. Seldom is any effort made responsibly to answer —possibly because no one really can.

But it seems reasonable to believe that until we are able to isolate and define the underlying causes, we will not be able intelligently to grapple with them.

I cannot assume to delineate all of the underlying causes, but my rather extensive readings, observations, meditations, and experiences have convinced me that a major one is that, in some way, our anchors have been torn from their moorings to changeless fundamental principles—among others, a decent respect for truth and for honesty, for the teachings of history, for the Ten Commandments, and the Golden Rule—and, without those anchors, we have simply lost our way.

This has caused distress, and in our distress we have tended to divide into ideological groups, and then one group began to blame another for our plight, and naturally this brought retaliatory responses in kind. That conduct continued to accelerate in pace and tempo until the pitch of tensions ran so high as to produce a running acrimonious and recriminatory dialogue that has dissipated mutual respect, engendered hatreds, and made nearly impossible any calm and conciliatory discussion of differences, and, hence, has precluded return and re-anchor to these changeless fundamentals.

As we have seen, that dialogue has largely sacrificed honest appeals to reason for other techniques. One of those has been the intentional and repeated misuse and distortion of good generic words and phrases in our language with the obvious design of giving them a gloss of meaning that casts their inherent odious implications from themselves to their opponents—a pretty slick trick to confuse unsuspecting people. Another has been arguments by catchwords of dubious meaning and sometimes of odious implications, that appeal not to reason but to prejudices and passions, and still another has been the use in arguments of meaningless, and often aspersionistic, clichés.

When we realize that such preachments have been nearly endlessly made, printed, and circulated as matters of truth, we can hardly wonder what the people, who must largely rely upon what they hear and read for their information, have been misled and are now confused and bewildered and at a loss to know whom or what they may safely believe and support.

Illustrative of the techniques used in glossing and distorting generic words and phrases, let me give you one or two concrete examples.

Frequently in this dialogue, some participants, while advocating—often quite covertly—"changes" in our forms and institutions of government, refer to their conservative opponents as "mossbacks," and, often in the same breath, as "radicals" or "extremists."

Although Webster says that "a conservative" is one who "favors retention of existing institutions and forms of government," the term has been, by intentional misuse, glossed to mean not one who would "retain" but one who would change, not necessarily by constitutional processes but even by usurpation and erosion, our "existing institutions and forms of government"—just the very antithesis of the dictionary sense of the term.

I refer to Webster only because I regard him as non-controversial. Webster says that the term "a leftist" means "a member of a radical or revolutionary party; a radical," and that the term "a rightist" means "a conservative," yet, by the intentional and repeated misuse of those terms "a leftist" has been glossed to mean "a conservative"—one who would "retain," not change, our existing institutions—and that a "rightist" is a "radical"—one who would change, not "retain," our existing institutions and forms of government—again, just the opposite of the dictionary sense of those terms.

These two simple examples are enough to reveal the technique—doubtless already familiar to most of you—that is being commonly used not to inform the people but to confuse and bewilder them.

I turn now to the technique of arguing by catchwords. Some of those that are commonly heard are of fairly definite meaning, but even they are often used with little fidelity to their true meanings. Others are advanced as terms of definite meaning, or of art, when in fact, as often used, they are meaningless.

We hear much confused argument revolving around the terms "discrimination," "segregation," "desegregation," and "integration," so I think it may be well briefly to consider what they really mean.

The dictionary sense of the term "discrimination" is

also, in the abstract, its legal sense. In its constitutional sense, it is one of the things prohibited to the states by the Fourteenth Amendment's guarantee of "the equal protection of the laws."

The term "segregation" is, in legal effect, only a synonym for constitutionally prohibited "discrimination." The term "desegregation" is a coined one of awkward and dubious meaning.

But the term "integration"—a term of no constitutional significance—though commonly used as a synonym of "antidiscrimination" or "antisegregation," literally has a very different meaning, and embraces the concept of amalgamation—well illustrated by the transfer of school children from their home district to a distant district for the purpose not of avoiding unconstitutional "discrimination" but rather for the purpose of affirmatively "mixing" or "integrating" the races—when, indeed, no provision of the Constitution so requires.

But in recent times we have seen obvious attempts to torture the word "integration" into a meaning synonymous with constitutionally prohibited "segregation," when, in truth, those terms speak entirely different concepts.

One of the devices most currently in use to accomplish this purpose is argument through the use of the coined phrase "de facto segregation." What does it mean? It means, if I understand the term, segregation in fact, whether by design or by accident.

There is, of course, a clear basis in the fundamental law of our land, particularly in the Fourteenth Amendment, for striking down state acts of "discrimination," and hence also of "segregation," in all public institutions, including state public schools, as violative of that Amendment's guarantee of the equal protection of the laws. But, as I have said, there is no provision in the Constitution which, in terms or reasonable intendment, compels "integration" of the races.

We also hear much confused argument about the term "civil rights." What does that term mean in the abstract? It is often used as one of definite meaning or of art. But the truth is that the term "civil rights" is not a term of art, and, when abstractly used, really has no concrete meaning. Again returning to Webster, he says that "civil rights" are "nonpolitical rights," and that, in the United States, the term means "rights secured by the Thirteenth and Fourteenth Amendments to the Constitution, and by certain implementing Acts of Congress, abolishing the incidences of involuntary servitude."

Now I should have thought that in Kansas, at least from a time that antedates the creation of this great University, all men had civil rights, for involuntary servitude was never practiced here—certainly not since the Emancipation Proclamation. Thus, the only meaning of the term, in the abstract, that even approaches concreteness is that "civil rights" are the rights of all men in the United States to be free from "the incidences of involuntary servitude."

We have now in America, at least four so-called Civil Rights Acts and another is in the hopper. It is clear that Civil Rights Acts like all other legislative acts derive their sense from what they say, from their terms, and not from what they are called.

Similarly, we hear much discussion in these days on the subject of "public accommodations." The term "public accommodations" is composed of plain, simple, generic words, yet many of us appear to be confused in our understanding, and hence unclear in our use, of the phrase. Now what does the phrase mean? Surely the term "public" accommodations does not include "private" accommodations. Surely public and private are not synonyms but are antonyms. "Public" things are those that are owned or controlled by the public and are usually supported by taxes, state or federal, and in which, therefore, every citizen has the same right of use and enjoyment.

But, by the same token, property that is privately owned and operated, paid for and maintained by private funds, is "private" property to which only those who are expressly or impliedly invited may, of right, come and enter. And surely this implies that any such invitation, like any other invitation, may be revoked by the owner at any time for any reason satisfactory to him alone.

Yet, almost daily, we see efforts—some of them temporarily successful and all of them confusing—to expand the concept of "public" to include that which is "private," such as a citizen's privately owned and operated store, his shop, his restaurant, his motel, yes, even his farm, and more recently his medical office and now also his law office, and to make those generically "private" facilities subject, as of right, to use and enjoyment by the public, under the tortured concept of "public accommodations."

I do not readily think of a better example of what is happening to our language and to our ability to communicate with certainty than is illustrated by our difficulties in maintaining the generic and basic distinction between what is "public"—and therefore subject to use by the public—and what is "private"—and therefore subject to use only by the owner or with his consent.

Another facet of current discussions revolves around the word "equality." We proudly say that our government is founded upon the concept that "all men are created equal." But we seem to be unclear as to the scope and breadth of the phrase—as to whether it means that all men must be accepted by all other men as "social equals," and as to whether it means that all men must be made and kept "economically equal," as an obligation of government.

Some, doubtless well-meaning, well-intentioned, good people have been arguing that it should be made the legal obligation of every man socially to accept every other man. However laudable may be the underlying objective, it is abundantly clear, from experience and from the nature of man, that this cannot be done by law, and that such an attempt is not a proper function of government. It is said that you can lead a horse to water, but you cannot make him drink. And that argument is sometimes parried with the statement, "But you can make him wish he had." And, in turn, that argument is parried with the further one, "So doing won't help his attitude or make him like you." That is what is really involved—a matter of mutual respect and liking. Any attempt to compel by law one man socially to accept another man can only agitate prejudices, stiffen resistance, and serve to impede and delay social acceptance. Social acceptance is a matter of developmental mutual respect and liking, and this cannot be brought about by force. These are matters of the heart, and it cannot be controlled by force. No minority group that has settled in our land has obtained—or likely ever will obtain—general acceptance and amalgamation here until, by long years of exemplary conduct, a *majority* of its members have earned the respect and liking of the people generally. And when that's done, the process is easy. This has been the experience of every race that has been amalgamated here. Never, until now, at least, has any race had the false help of legal force in amalgamating here. Any effort to *compel* social acceptance by the force of a criminal law, would be self-defeating—a step in the wrong direction.

There are well-meaning persons among us, good people again, who argue that the proper concept of "equality" is that all men are entitled to be assured, by and at the expense of the government—which means by their brothers—of permanent economic equality.

To argue that all men are entitled, at the expense of their brothers, to permanent economic equality, is to argue for the adoption of communism, which, Webster says, means "a system of social organization in which all goods are held in common," and, hence, in which all men are by law made and kept economically equal. Do those who so advocate understand this? I doubt that they do, and, for obvious reasons, I prefer to believe that they do not.

But the government established here by our fore-fathers—and early said to be the finest instrument of government ever conceived by the minds of man and I think still is—is not of that kind. It is, instead, a Democratic-Republic guaranteeing free enterprise and the right to earn and possess private capital. It is not, and was never intended to be, a leveler of men. Quite the contrary. It was intended to permit, and it does permit, the ambitious, energetic, creative, and thrifty men, by honest efforts, to improve their lot as much as they can, even if others choose not to try. It does not intend to destroy initiative and ambition by holding accomplishments down to the level of the least ambitious.

While individuals—and I bear heavily on the word *individuals*—have the legal right to discriminate between our people, the government has no such right. Hence, under our government, the term "equality" must mean, essentially, that government, state and federal, cannot and must not deny to any citizen (1) the equal opportunity to obtain equal schooling, (2) the right to equal governmental treatment, (3) the right to equal justice, (4) the equal right of suffrage, and (5) the consequent right to equal opportunity.

But the right to equal opportunity, if indeed it is to be equal, must include the opportunity to develop and prove unequal talents. Any other concept would destroy the natural incentive of every man to improve his lot by holding him down to the unambitious level of the mediocre or below, which inevitably would result in the society's decadence.

In the same connection, we hear much discussion of "public welfare." This has become a sanctified phrase. And if you challenge, however soundly, those who wave its banner, they are likely to call you a bigot.

Some seem to feel that it is the legal obligation of the government to finance the needs of every citizen. Some even suggest that our national Constitution so contemplates, but nothing could be further from the truth. In the Preamble of our Constitution, our founding fathers, in describing one of the purposes of their efforts, used the term to "promote the General Welfare," but this was to be done, as they said, in the ways and by the means set forth in the body of the document, and one will search it in vain for any evidences of any delegation, by the States or the people, of any power to the national government to dip into the Federal treasury for the individual support of private citizens. Thus, the privilege, and the moral obligation, to determine when, and how much, aid should be given to the deserving needy among them and who they are, like all other privileges and powers that were not delegated to the national government by the States, was reserved to the States and the people.

I now turn to the misleading, and therefore dangerous techniques of current argument by clichés. Some would-be leaders have been voicing slogans and clichés which, in instances, appear on the surface to be logical, and some even religious, but which in truth are neither. Instead they are dangerously deceptive and destructive. They appeal not to reason, but to passions and to prejudices.

One is: "Government owes every citizen a living." This is the false cry of the prideless lazy. Inasmuch as the food, shelter, and clothing necessary for his "living" can only be produced by the labors of someone, this is a cry for support by the sweat of another man's brow.

A second is: "Human rights, not property rights." Are these rights in any way inconsistent or mutually destructive? Is not the right to have and be protected in property a valuable "human right"? Are not those rights actually mutually consistent and even dependent? Any thoughtful observation of history will reveal that where private property rights have not been respected and protected there has not been what we have chosen recently to call "human rights." Private property rights are the soil in which our concept of human rights grows and matures. As long as private property rights are secure, human rights will be respected and will endure and evolve.

A third is the Russian-coined phrase—and do not mistake its origin—"Production is for use, not for profits." Must it be wholly for the one or the other? Is it not truly for both? Is there any inconsistency or immorality in producing useful things at a profit? If production is not to yield a profit, there will be no incentive to produce. And if there is no incentive to produce, there will be no production for use. It is the incentive of profits that has produced the plentiful blessings of our nation and that has enabled it to grow, progress, and develop as it has. Reasonable profits are essential to the survival of free enterprise, and, hence, of our society. If the state were to take over under the slogan of "use, not profits," initiative would be destroyed, progress would be halted, and soon stagnation would set in and destroy our society.

A fourth of these clichés—and of which we hear much these days—is: "Obey the good laws, but not the bad ones"; and a fifth one—that should be considered with the fourth—is: "Action now, not the delays of the law." Is not each of these clichés a call for anarchy? Does not the fourth invite men to violate the laws they do not like? And does not the fifth invite men to spurn the courts and all constituted authority and to take the law not into their hearts, but into their own hands? And if we allow man to disobey with impunity the laws they do not like, or to spurn the courts and all constituted authority by taking the law, or what they think ought to be the law, into their own hands, will we not be inviting anarchy and chaos?

Yet this is precisely what some self-appointed leaders, not just racial leaders but also many others, have been advocating, and it is precisely what their followers have been doing. Aroused by these techniques, those followers frequently have assembled, from far and wide—often, unfortunately, with the encouragement and even at the expense of well-meaning but legally uninformed and misguided churchmen and church organizations—into large and loosely assembled groups, or mobs, to wage what they have called "demonstrations" for the purpose of *forcing* the grant of what they call "rights"—always unspecified—in defiance of the law, of the courts, and of all constituted authority.

At the beginning, these "demonstrations" consisted of episodic group invasions and appropriations of private stores, first by sitting down and later by lying down therein, and, eventually, by blocking the entrances thereto with their limp bodies.

Seeing that those trespasses were often applauded in high places, and generally were not stopped or punished, but, rather, were appeased and rewarded, those leaders and their groups quickly enlarged the scope of their activities by massing and marching their followers on the sidewalks, the streets, highways and publicways—frequently blocking and appropriating them to a degree that precluded their intended public uses.

And that conduct, too, being nearly always appeased, the process spread areawise, as might have been expected, from one Southern city to another, and then into one Northern city after another, and, eventually, pretty generally throughout the whole of the land.

These "demonstrations" have been conducted under the banner of "peaceable civil disobedience," and also under the claim of protection by the peaceable-assembly-and-petition provisions of the First Amendment to the United States Constitution. But the fact is that most of these claims were, and are, untrue. Let me demonstrate.

"Crime," says Webster, means "an act or omission forbidden by law and punishable upon conviction." It cannot be denied that many of those trespasses violated the criminal trespass laws of the local jurisdictions involved, nor that those laws impose penalties for their violation, and, hence, that those trespasses constituted "crimes."

Now, in the first place, that conduct cannot honestly be termed "peaceable," for we all know that the assembly and incitement of a large group or mob for the avowed purpose of *forcing* direct action outside the law amounts to the creation of a mob bent on lawlessness, and is inherently disturbing to the peace of all others.

In the second place, that conduct cannot honestly be termed "civil disobedience," for the simple reason, which I think anyone should be able to understand, that *willful violation of the criminal laws* is "criminal disobedience," not "civil disobedience."

And, lastly, those criminal trespasses are not protected by the peaceable-assembly-and-petition provisions of the First Amendment.

That provision is doubtless well known to all of you, but let me recall to you what it says—in pertinent part: "Congress shall make no law . . . abridging . . . the right of the people peaceably to assemble and to petition the government for a redress of grievance."

Now, obviously, nothing in that language grants a license to any man, or group of men, to violate our criminal laws—including those which prohibit trespass upon, and appropriation of, private property, as well as those prohibiting the willful obstruction of public ways.

Rather, as Mr. Justice Roberts wrote upon the subject in 1939, in the case of Hage against C.I.O., "The privilege of a citizen of the United States to use the streets and parks for communication of views on national questions must be regulated in the interest of all; it is not absolute, but is relative, and must be exercised in subordination to the general comfort and convenience, and always in consonance with peace and good order. . . ."

Surely, no thoughtful person will disagree with that statement, nor with the one recently made by the President of Yale University, in a speech at Detroit, "that the current rash of demonstrations make a ludicrous mockery of the democratic debating process."

The philosophy of "obeying only the laws you like" and attempting to rule by force has given rise to mobs and mob actions that have proven—as certainly we should have expected—to be tailor-made for infiltration, take-over, and use by rabble-rousers, radicals, Communists, and the like, some of whom are avowedly bent on the breakdown of law, order, and morality in our society, and, hence, on its destruction. And we now see that virtually all such "demonstrations" are being infiltrated by rabble-rousers and radicals—many of them by Communists—and that they not infrequently break into open violence. That's their inherent nature and tendency.

Even though those results may not have been contemplated, and surely weren't wished, by those Americans who advocated disobedience of our laws, nevertheless they did advocate that philosophy and they did put its processes into action, and cannot now escape the consequences of, or the responsibility for, the results.

Seeing the appeasements and successes of that process in racial strife and in earlier labor strife, other would-be leaders have now adopted the process and have spread it into many other areas. It has now spread into the campuses of most of our great universities—very fortunately only slightly on this one—where, as in Berkeley, it has been used to commit assaults, to commit kidnappings, even kidnappings of peace officers, imprisonment of police officers, the commandeering of public address systems, and their use in spewing over the campus the most filthy of four-letter words, and in the general breakdown of law, order, and morality on that campus.

The process is also now progressively employed, by radicals and those who would give aid and comfort to our enemies, to hinder and impede our nation's effort to conduct the war in which we are involved—think of this—to impede our nation's effort to conscript the necessary military personnel, as witness the recent rash of draft card burners and the like—to impede our government's ability to move its troops and to supply them, by laying their limp bodies on the railroad rails, and generally in many devious ways, by traitorous placards and the like, impeding or trying to impede our nation's efforts to defend its international policies including the waging of the present war.

The process has now been extended even to efforts to thwart governmental, legislative, and executive action. Indeed, it would be hard to name a field that has escaped, or that is not vulnerable to, that process. What, I would ask you, has happened to our patriotism and to our sense of values?

These are but recent examples of history's teachings that the toleration of some crime encourages all crime, and it can hardly be denied that our toleration of these crimes of trespass, and worse, has been a contributing factor to the recent spread of criminal violence which Mr. J. Edgar Hoover, a man I greatly respect, says makes it impossible "for the citizens of this country to . . . walk the streets of our cities without [danger of] being mugged, raped, or robbed." He continued, "We can't do that today," and he added, "All through the country, almost without exception, this condition prevails."

The great pity here is that these minority groups, in preaching and practicing defiance of the law and the courts, are, in fact, eroding our legal structure which alone can ever assure to them due process of law and the equal protection of the laws, and that can, thus, protect them from discrimination and abuses by majorities. It is under these legal processes, slow as they sometimes are, that all the gains of all history by minority groups have been brought about. Although the processes of the law are slow, the courts are deliberative bodies that hear and weigh carefully before they decide, and their judgments are most likely to be just. In all events, there is not now, and history shows there has never been, a better way of deciding issues that arise between men.

We have all been often told, and many of us have preached, that crime does not pay, but the recent rash and spread of law defiance, and the successes—however tenuous and temporary—of that philosophy in attaining goals, seems to compel a reappraisal of that concept, for, from what we see currently happening, one reasonably could believe that certain types of crimes are being permitted to pay.

Indeed, official encouragement often has been given, even, at times, in some high places, to conduct these "demonstrations," which have led to the commission of these criminal trespasses, and it can hardly be denied that they have been rather widely tolerated.

It is undoubtedly true, as recited in the theme of the presidentially proclaimed Law Day, 1965, that "a citizen's first duty is to uphold the law." But it is also the first duty of government to enforce the law. As said in an article in the April 10, 1965, issue of the magazine *America*, "[Government] has no right to turn the cheek of its citizens. Instead, it is gravely obligated—obligated by the very purpose of its existence—to see to their protection."

Surely the great majority of Americans agree with the May, 1965, public statement of Mr. Lewis F. Powell, then president of the American Bar Association, that "America needs a genuine revival of respect for law and orderly processes, a reawakening of individual responsibility, a new impatience with those who violate and circumvent laws, and a determined insistence that laws be enforced, courts respected, and due process followed."

I would like to conclude, as I began, with a plea for a return to simple honesty, responsibility and forthrightness in our public speakings and writings—that they may honestly inform and not misinform the people—and for a return to an orderly society where law is obeyed, if not respected, and that we assure this obedience by the prompt, impartial, evenhanded, certain, and substantial punishment of all persons whose willful conduct violates those laws—and that we do so promptly, and, I would hope, before mass crime gets, as it surely can, so far out of hand as to be beyond the curbing capacities of our peace-keeping agencies and authorities.

Just one last word of historical reminder and I'm through: you all recall that in his farewell address the Father of our Country told us that the Constitution of the United States may not prove to be a perfect document and that if, in experience, it develops to be, in any particular, wrong, then let it freely be amended, but always by the people and in the manner that the instrument designates, and never be erosion or usurpation, for let it not be forgotten that those are the means by which Constitutional governments have historically been destroyed. To this I say, Amen.

COMMENTARIES

LARSON: I heartily applaud. If we cannot depend upon the meaning of words as between human beings, then it is going to become virtually impossible not only to have a civilization at all but more specifically to have a rule of law among people. I'd like, therefore, to examine two or three examples used by Mr. Whittaker to expand a bit upon some of these basic principles.

First, I would like to come to the defense of Deane Malott when he referred to poverty as being one of the stark problems threatening peace and order in the world. I don't think Mr. Malott was referring to the relative state of poverty in the United States compared with a century ago. We all know that this is the most affluent society ever known to man. I'm sure that what he was referring to was the dangerous contrast between the

affluence of this country on the one hand and the extreme
poverty in about two-thirds of the world. I heard Arnold Toynbee
say recently that two-thirds of the people of the world are
still living under conditions not essentially different from what
they were five thousand years ago. The average income in most
of South and Southeast Asia is between a dime and a quarter
a day. It isn't getting very much better, and the gap between
the rich and the poor is widening and not narrowing. This I
think is the meaning of the word "poverty" that was intended
when it was used by President Malott.

I think the term "public accommodations" needs a little
discussion, because this is a good illustration of the very point
that Mr. Whittaker was making. The term "public accommodations" is used in one of the titles of the Civil Rights Act
of 1964, and what it means is not an accommodation owned
by a public body such as a governmental body, but an
accommodation opened to the public whether or not owned
by private citizens, in fact, most of the time owned by private
citizens. I would suggest to you that this is as legitimate and
colloquial a use of the word public as the one mentioned by
Mr. Whittaker, which is "something operated by the government." In any case, this is the meaning chosen by the
legislators, because they very carefully define in the Civil
Rights Act of 1964 title precisely what they mean by "public
accommodations" and they mean "accommodations open to
the public." In line with the dictum in *Alice in Wonderland*,
the Legislature has said, "This word means what I mean it to
mean, no more, no less."

What the Congress meant by public accommodations then
is perfectly legitimate. They have brought in deliberately all
kinds of privately owned establishments. They've brought in
theaters, they've brought in recreational areas, they've brought in
hotels, motels, restaurants, eating places, lunch counters, and all
the rest. They've done so deliberately and they've done so not
in spite of the fact but because of the fact they are privately
owned.

The only significance this choice of words might possibly
have would be the constitutional basis for this kind of action.
The public accommodations title is not based upon the concept
of state action referred to by Mr. Justice Whittaker at all, and

so it doesn't make any difference whether the accommodations are publicly or privately owned. It's based upon the interstate commerce powers of the Congress, on a very wide interpretation of them to be sure, to which the United States Supreme Court has had its share in contributing. But this is an illustration of how you can make proper use of the word if you take the trouble to define it at the time you use it, as has been done with this term "public accommodation." You can quarrel if you like with the policy of extending this degree of control over privately owned hotels, motels, restaurants, and the like, but there isn't any problem here so far as the use of the word is concerned because it is perfectly clear in the act what it means.

I'd like to hasten, however, to the main substance of the last part of Mr. Justice Whittaker's remarks, because it seemed to me here we come to an issue that has got to have some discussion if the record is to be left in the proper state of clarity. This is his discussion of the lawlessness that has attended the civil rights movement.

Whatever may have been the case leading up to the present state of law in this country, including the sit-ins and the lunch counter demonstrations, the first ones of which, by the way, took place in Durham, North Carolina, where I now reside, for the most part the law now is on the side of the civil rights workers and everything they stand for. We've got a public accommodations clause in the civil rights act, we've got a voting rights act, we've got a Civil Rights Act of 1964, we've got a twelve-year-old Supreme Court decision, *Brown* v. *Board of Education* which laid the basis for desegregation of school. The law has been on the side of people who are insisting on these rights. The illegality is almost 98 per cent the other way around now.

True, we have witnessed defiance of law in this country on a deplorable scale, but, with the exception of a certain amount of blocking of highways here and there because perhaps of the high-handed deprivation of parade permits and so on, the great bulk of it is in the form of refusal of people to obey the law of the land in the form of these two major acts, the Civil Rights Act of 1964, and the Voting Rights Act of 1965, the continuing refusal to desegregate the schools, the continuing refusal to desegregate theaters and eating places and the like in various parts of the South, the continued refusal to register voters—and here we have to do with the most precious right of the American citizen politically. True, there has been illegality on both sides and I deplore it on both sides. I don't like the illegality of some of the things that go on at the Berkeley campus. But let's get our dimensions and our proportions straight.

What is a sit-down at a lunch counter compared to a century of deprivation of voting rights? What is a certain amount of roughhousing in connection with demonstrations, compared with a whole series of civil rights murders? How many people have been murdered by civil rights workers compared with the civil rights workers who have been murdered? How many churches have been burned by Negroes compared with the Negro churches that have been burned? Let's be concerned about illegality wherever it occurs, and I think if we were to weigh these illegalities the scales would tip today very heavily in this direction.

There's a very curious thing about the defiance of law in connection with civil rights and any other kind of movement for that matter that I think should be pointed out. It is not the demonstration generally that produces the result. It is the reaction to the demonstration which is usually more violent and more illegal than the demonstration itself and for that reason is more counterproductive. If when the march to Montgomery was projected, Governor Wallace had said, "Come one, come all. Come on and use the highways," if there had been no cattle prods, no bull-whips, no violence, no civil rights murders, we wouldn't have had the civil rights acts we have today. I'm just as sure of that as I am of anything.

It was the murder of three civil rights workers in Mississippi that gave us the Civil Rights Act of 1964; it was the murder of Mrs. Liuzzo that gave us the Voting Rights Act of 1965. It's almost as direct as that, because public resentment and reaction to the outrages produced just the opposite of the results that the people resisting these changes hoped to bring about. The very self-appointed guardians of states' rights by their violent reactions and their illegal reactions to these various demonstrations have drawn down over their own heads these two acts which cut into states rights far more deeply than anybody ever would have dreamed possible five or ten years ago. So this then,

I think, is the criticism and the comment that needs to be made at this point to restore a sense of balance.

I agree wholeheartedly with the final conclusion of Mr. Justice Whittaker that we ought to have an evenhanded, firm, courageous, and all-out enforcement of our laws, but I caution that if this were done in some parts of the South and in some states in the South, there wouldn't be enough restaurants left to feed the populace out of jail and there wouldn't be enough theater proprietors left to keep the entertainment business going, and, as for the government, there wouldn't be enough public officials left outside of jail to run one county.

EISELEY: I will not speak of the legal aspects of what I am not competent to speak upon, but those of you who heard me speak yesterday will remember that I had something to say about social institutions and the degree of flexibility necessary to maintain themselves and serve the purposes of society without becoming barriers to progress and thereby generating explosive forces in society. I would like to begin with a personal anecdote that I think has a bearing upon attitudes toward us in many parts of the world today.

In the thirties when I was attending graduate school, I lived at the International House in Philadelphia and had friends who were Japanese, Indians, Philippinos, and Chinese. One day a little group of us decided to go to Washington for the day to look about this capital, which was to become one of the great international capitals of the world. We had expected to return in the evening, but some car trouble developed and I set out to obtain for my friends and myself shelter for the night. We went to one hotel after the other and were politely turned away. Finally, I went to the YMCA where we were also refused; it was amazing how crowded Washington was that day. By then my friends were beginning to look more and more embarrassed. Finally we reached the outskirts of town and I thought perhaps one of the local residential areas that took in automobile visitors might accommodate us. We stopped before a residence with a sign out, and I went up to the door with one of my Chinese friends. A harsh-faced woman appeared, and I asked for a room. The rest of the boys were sitting out in the car at this time, and she looked interested, showing signs of having room

to take us in. Suddenly, however, she looked at my Chinese
friend and said to me, "Is this your man?" In my utter
naïvete I said, "No, he is my friend," and at that point the
woman slammed the door. My friends were foreign guests of
this great nation, men destined to go home to China, to the
Philippines—one of those men died at Bataan, later. This,
unfortunately, was their reception in the capital of the United
States; this was the reception of people who were carrying home
an American education, this was their experience in the white
man's country.

We went back to Philadelphia to a small Chinese restaurant
in a depressed area. We had dinner there late, and I felt that my
complexion was changing, that there was a growing feeling of
resentment in me against white men, and, groping in this
situation, so charged with emotion, I said to my friends who
were all sitting looking at their plates rather gloomily, "I want
to apologize for my country." We can say what we will of
how long it takes for a people, for any people, in some fashion
to justify themselves so that they are socially acceptable
elsewhere, but at that point how was America justifying itself to
people of other races all over the world in terms of reasonable
contact, association, and living together in peace and amity?
I would merely comment that if people have to wait too long,
if there is not this "sway" in social institutions through the
centuries, which keeps them viable and open to change, then
explosive violence is liable, at some point, to emerge. It is the
institution with, at the same time, stability and "give," as at
the top of a skyscraper, that sustains the schism.

There is also the problem of the individual that I mentioned
to you yesterday, this question of whither we are going as
individuals. I can recall a man whom I knew well, who, after
escaping, entered Nazi Germany, time after time after time to
rescue other people at the risk of his own life. A whole nation
had taken a point of view so intolerable to his personal moral
sense that he fought it to the end. And I think that we as
human beings have got to accept some of this responsibility. I,
too, am for law and order. I, too, am aware that in these
violences that grow up there is frequently difficulty in terms of
distinguishing between black and white, in terms of morality and
justice, but I would beg us to remember that words themselves,

about which a great deal has been said here by Justice Whittaker, come down the long traverse of time as rolled and pounded as a hand-axe in a riverbed. They change, and a certain degree of flexibility in words is inevitable, and in fact, if we are to communicate from generation to generation, it is important that words take new inflections and that they change. At the same time I recognize quite well that in the process vibrations are set up in a rapidly changing society in which advantage can be taken of words by the demagogue.

MONTAGU: In relation to what Dr. Eiseley said about his experience with his Chinese friend, I think a large number of us have had similar experiences in this country. I remember hearing on television a man who kept a restaurant on the Baltimore-Washington-New York Turnpike who had refused an African diplomat service in his restaurant. He explained his conduct by saying that the Constitution of the United States guaranteed him the right to do what he liked and he did it. Now I suggest that the Constitution of the United States, or any Constitution of any kind, never guaranteed anyone the right to do what he likes. Americans, of course, frequently misinterpret the Constitution to mean just this; but what freedom is I think was beautifully said by Lord Acton, a Catholic, English historian who said that freedom is not the liberty to do what you would like, but the right to be able to do what you ought. And in that connection I would say, with all due respect to Justice Whittaker, that the law is not so inflexible that it is incapable of change, that times do change the conditions under which human beings live, and that the law—not being the ass that it has so often been described as being—must recognize this, and that if the law itself does not recognize this the people should. Mr. Justice Whittaker has said that there are people who say good laws should be obeyed but bad laws should not be obeyed, and he disapproved of this statement. I would with respect cite to Justice Whittaker the individual who fired that shot at Lexington which is still reverberating around the world and respectfully suggest that if he had taken Mr. Whittaker's view of the law, that man would have been hanged. Certainly the Father of our Country to whom he referred would have been hanged by the British, and Mr. Franklin and Mr. Jefferson would

also have been strung up. I heartily applaud the conduct of
these fellow Americans who protested unjust laws even though
they were laws, and I heartily support the Berkeley students
and the civil disobedience of the large number of Americans
who considered that such statements as Mr. Justice Whittaker
made here—namely, that a majority of a minority group have
to earn the respect and the liking of the people—represent
the sheerest hyprocrisy and nonsense. I would refer Mr. Justice
Whittaker to Sir Thomas Noon Tolfourd, an English judge
who said, "Fill the seats of justice with good men, but not so
absolute in goodness as to forget what human frailty is."
And I would also suggest to Mr. Justice Whittaker that he
acquaint himself with the elementary facts about injustice and
wrongs and the evils that Americans have practiced for 350
years against Negroes whom they have held down in the mud.
To expect them to earn the liking of people who themselves have
become dirty because they have held them down in the mud
for 350 years is again the sheerest hypocrisy. Let us first do what
we ought to do and redress the wrongs we have done against
these people in particular. When Mr. Justice Whittaker said
that permanent economic equality at the expense of government
is Communism, I would suggest to him that what we need to
do is to follow the Communist in Jesus Christ, who also was
one of the first breakers of the law and one of the greatest of all
trouble-makers, and redress the wrongs that we have done against
these people by proposing that the government set up a federal
project which will economically make some recompense for
these wrongs in the billions of dollars, so that we at any rate
can stand before the bars of humanity, as we cannot at this
moment, with some sort of decency. As Americans we will
either fall or stand on this issue of what we do about equality,
especially for those people we have wronged for so many years.

MAN AND THE FUTURE | 4

PROSPECTS FOR HUMANITY

R. Buckminster Fuller

When I use the term "Prospects for Humanity," I believe that there are many ways in which man can go. It is possible today to assess some of the large trend-patterns now emerging and their relationship to those great potentials of mankind that are evident.

I am doing with you today something that I learned to do throughout a great part of my life. I never allow myself to prepare talks, because I've learned that it is perfectly possible to think out loud and I know that if somebody comes to speak to me and pulls a paper out of his pocket and starts to read me a speech, I say, "Let me have that. I can read it more rapidly than you can. My hearing is not very good anyway." Whatever preparation I have must come realistically from my whole life and not just a few hours of special case collecting and putting together of notes. What I like about human meetings is what we are able to do to one another. I am confident that it is possible to think out loud before a large group of human beings and have two-way communication even though I am the only one formulating sound words.

Last year we were all made very thoroughly aware of the feelings of the young world by the University of California's 1964-65 New Year's Berkeley Campus outbreak. Many were shocked by the inquiry by reporters of these students which indicated that the young people did not feel particular loyalty to their families, to their university, or to their country. Further inquiry of these young people showed their loyalty is to the world. They are "world minded," ergo, nationally unbiased. In the prime of life, realizing their first individual independence and bursting with logical and realistic idealism, these students are everywhere confronted with yesterday's science fiction, now operative as today's practical reality. Also, these students find themselves confronted with the concurrent news that the majority of the world's people are still faced with starvation, ignorance, and suffering.

I have the good fortune to be invited to many universities as I travel around the world. I have now visited one hundred and seventy-four universities and colleges around the world, and a number of them a number of times. I say "good fortune," because this keeps me in close contact with the young world. During the last year, at the universities and colleges when I have had the opportunity to select the age group that I would deal with, I have purposely selected the group of the age of discontent at Berkeley. During my visits, we have talked a great deal about their lives. These young people were born the year of the Hiroshima atomic bomb explosion. That's quite a birthmark. One may well wonder at their feelings towards their parents and their society. We find that the young world questions our side's undertaking to blow up large, large numbers of humanity.

The present junior and senior class university students, everywhere around the earth, are World War II babies. Most frequently, as babies, their fathers were away at the war and their mothers away at the munitions works. The superlative wartime spirit of social cooperation which must have inspired the children's foster parents and baby sitters to undertake the care and nurturing of those babies must have satisfied to a unique degree the babies' and children's innate trust. This innate trust is the most critical and easily damaged of all the socially coordinate, spontaneous behaviorisms of new born life, which, if damaged, usually results in school dropouts and juvenile delinquency.

The World War II babies' subsequent childhoods were spent with their "G. I." student parents at universities. The attempt of their parents to learn more, to speak better, to use their heads instead of their muscles to earn their livelihoods was, as has been proven by the behavioral sciences, a most powerful influence on their children's favorable development of intelligence. We have learned that one of the greatest effects on the brain of the new life as it develops and as its various capabilities come into play is whether these capabilities are kept active and useful. Whether they get pinched off depends a great deal upon the speech patterns of the parents. Human life is born ugly-helpless and part of the invention of being born ugly-helpless is having that life taken care of. There is an extraordinary nervous relationship between the new life lying ugly-helpless and those who are supposedly going to look out for it. Even though the child may not understand the words of its parents, if the child lying there hears drunken parents in a quarrel or a mother about to leave home, you have a certified dropout on your hands later. The child is tremendously aware of intent in even the tone of voice of the parents.

The twenty-one year olds of 1966 are also the first babies reared by the "third parent," television. Television is everywhere around the world. In the slums of Hong Kong and Caracas, the television antennas are bristling. Somehow the people get hold of second- or third-hand T.V. sets and get them going. There is a relationship to the young life everywhere through television. The young life finds television in the home, and it is a new and interesting kind of foster parent because this grandmother can be turned on or off as she entertains you or not. The children recognize the actors on television who play one day in one part and the next day in another, and children are used to and love play acting so that they don't take what the television actor is saying very seriously. But what they do pay attention to is that he is trying to say things clearly.

We have learned from the behavioral sciences that when parents are trying to formulate their own thoughts, reaching for the right words and trying to improve their vocabulary and thereby their speech efficiency, the children are inclined to do so also. If the parents are accepting the cliché from the local bar and not trying to do their own thinking, the child begins to stop using its brain. What the children notice then on the television is that everyone who earns his job on the television does so by having good vocabulary and good diction: he is trying very hard to do his part well even though he may be selling a product that he obviously doesn't care very much about. The children can tell that it is a sort of game and have great confidence in these characters. The parents come home at the end of their working day and say that they have had a terrible time at the store, have a cocktail, and the kids go back and turn on the third parent to see what the world news is. Television brings the children world news with greater frequency and precision than the children received their milk.

For this reason, this television-reared generation thinks "world." They think and demand justice for all humanity without exception, and with the natural idealism of young life, feel very badly about the world because it is not being run properly. They have learned about the new inventions that have been made practical during their own span of years. I have already enumerated them one by one for the senior class of today so that I shall not discuss again all of the past twenty-one years, but I would like to point out that these years are filled with going under the polar ice in the submarine, going completely around the world without surfacing or running into anything, climbing Mount Everest, going to the bottom of the Pacific Ocean five miles towards the center of the earth and photographing the bottom, photographing the other side of the moon, overcoming viruses, etc., etc. The young people say, "obviously, we can do anything." And then they realize that man is not doing well and that their parents are short-sightedly preoccupied by only local affairs. The world is in a mess and still the young inherently know that the world can be made to work. And that young world is without bias and prejudice: it hasn't had much experience yet, it hasn't any ideas about how to make the world work, but it certainly concludes that the older people have been making a mess of it. Out of thousands of possible examples, they see the thoughtless destruction of the land profile and the ecological balance by the bulldozer, with the real estators running entire communities and the planners completely without authority. They find short-sighted local expediency getting ready to ruin the world and that their own children will thereby not have much to look forward to. There is a strong and new movement toward a desire to plan constructively.

The new world is becoming extremely literate. The number who finish high school and go on to college is rising. Of all the curves plotted from the statistics of our society, one that is continually and sharply rising is the number of those who go on to higher education. All around the world, education is increasing. Today's young world is the most healthy and literate in history and able to look at and be concerned about the whole world. We may have more of a break coming between the old world and the new than at any moment before in history.

Now I would like to look at some other patterns.

In 1927, I began a new attack on problems. Due to earlier experiences that I had had in the regular navy with the early airplanes and the early electronics, I became convinced that a new kind of pattern was beginning to take shape. I left the navy in 1922 because our only child, born during World War I, caught the flu, developed spinal meningitis, then infantile paralysis, and just before her fourth birthday died of pneumonia. Before she died, I was in the Orient and I was allowed to resign from the navy in order to stay home near that child. Having become extremely familiar with advanced naval technology, I tended to feel that the very low order of technology and poor economic command of the individual on land made for a very inadequate land environment, and I blamed this environment and the very low level of knowledge operative in the medical world for the unnecessary death of my child. Even in 1922, the navy was able to fire a one-ton charge from a gun mounted on a toiling ship in heavy seas at another ship in motion and hit on the first slow clearing of the horizon. If the same kind of technological capabilities, costing millions and billions of dollars, used for armaments, were applied to making man physically successful, my child's death need not have occurred. My viewpoint has been vindicated: in the interim years both spinal meningitis and infantile paralysis, thought of as utterly incurable, have since become curable.

Another experience after my resignation from the navy was my entry into the building world. There, I developed a building technique that had been invented by my architect father-in-law. His invention was useful for building reinforced concrete structures in a novel and patentable manner.

I organized five factories for the manufacture of his building components and built 240 of his structures in the eastern half of the United States between 1922 and 1927. After having been in the advanced technologies of the navy, I became even more aware with this building industry experience of the fact that the home arts—the livingry arts—were millenniums behind the weaponry arts and were only being advanced as a by-product of the high-priority weapons race. Full of ignorance, the building world is anti-priority.

What could change the life of people on land was bringing the technology developed for sea and air weaponry into the domestic economy. The high performance technology developed for the production of weapons comes progressively to levels of obsolescence. For instance, a premier type of submarine or airplane finally becomes eclipsed by competition and therefore becomes obsolete. Second-grade weapons are worthless. The contractor who has been producing the obsolete item often finds himself failing to get the next contract for the newer kind of weapon or tool. However, the ex-contractors are tooled-up with powerful high-performance technology. They can produce a great deal with very little— i.e., with high performance per pound. For these obvious reasons the ex-government contractors look around in the domestic market to find ways in which to exploit their super-technical ability. The ex-government supplier thus brought the dynamo off of the battleship into the city to light man's streets, and the electric lights developed for the battleship came thereafter to replace the candles in our domestic candelabras although the candelabras themselves have perhaps not been redesigned.

The domestic economy was never made the comprehensive focus of general systems theory and the prime beneficiary of scientific knowledge. High performance technology is only progressively substituted for low or indifferent performance of the total structural and mechanical scheme of the forever-fortuitous, land-borne edifices. Parts may become improved without improvement in total concept of land-borne technology. Our television, radio, general electronics, refrigeration, desalinization, et al., have continually advanced the domestic economy, but only as second-hand gadgetry, by-producted by the cast-off segments of the weaponry industry.

Doing constantly more with ever less came from the world of seaborne, or airborne, weapons. To persist as a "winner" in the game of world armaments, a constantly accelerating evolution must be regeneratively initiated in specific improvements in performance per pounds of physical resources and per hours of scientific and technical expertise invested in a given task in order to be supreme in carrying the greatest hitting power the greatest distances in the shortest time, with ever increasing accuracy of aim and at ever higher degrees of energy efficiency.

The inception of the historical world around magnitude of seaborne and airborne armaments racing and outright warring began importantly a century ago with steam-driven, metal ships. In conjunction with the foregoing observation, we find that there is a fundamental technical requirement in the building of ships which is unknown or unused by builders of structures on dry land. The unique requirement is that the prime structure, the ship, has to float. As Archimedes showed, we can only float as much weight as the weight of the water the ship displaces. Therefore, in designing a ship, there is a specifically limited amount of weight to invest in each of the ship's many and various essential functions. As men became informed by their high seas storm and battle experiences, they developed more and more speed, hitting power, and cargo space with ever less of invested resources in time, material, and energy per each and every function of the ship and its equipment.

The technology that came from the sea has become greatly advanced in the technology of the air where performance per pound became of even greater importance. The heavier-than-air sky-ship requires directional velocity in order to develop the negative pressure or "lift" above its wingfoils. The airplane originally had to develop velocity at the cost of heavy engine and fuel. In the early days of the airplane so enormous a weight of fuel had to be carried through the sky that nothing else could be carried but the aviator himself. Just "getting there" was all that could be accomplished by a Lindbergh, but that was great. It was proof of fundamental feasibility which in time could be improved. The progressively improving performance per aircraft pound became exquisitely important in order to be able to earn additional weight capacity increments for the ultimate tasks of carrying weapons and later air passengers and general air cargos. Science set out to do something about it. In the first fifty years of the airplane two and a half trillion dollars went into direct and indirect subsidy of the airplane. Today, Lockheed is working on a 250-passenger ship which will fly at almost two thousand miles per hour, reaching any part of the world in two hours.

Building on land developed as the antithesis of ship building. The ship at sea was designed to attack; designed to do the most with the least. On land, man learned to protect himself from those less fortunate than he in producing food and goods, by constructing fortifications; the higher and thicker and heavier the walls, the more secure man felt. "Secure as the Rock of Gibralter" is the concept that motivated land structures. The end of this thinking came, incidentally, when the technology of the sea came up on the land during World War II in what is called the

"Blitz," and ran over the high, thick, and heavy national defense lines as though they didn't exist. That was the end of thinking that extra weight gives extra security, but still on the land today we do not think in terms of performance per pound. It comes as a complete surprise to the 99.9 per cent of humanity that live on the land that more can be done with less. This again is technology that came from the sea.

In contrast, building technology on dry land is rarely predicated upon total weight limitation. Displacement is not and never has been a prime consideration of dry land building. Architects therefore do not think in terms of weight displacements of buildings, nor in terms of performance per pound and energy expenditure ratios. The building industry today is still about 3000 years behind the technology of weaponry. You ask any architect what this building weighs. Could you tell me what this building weighs? Could you tell me within a hundred thousand tons? Within a million tons? You can't? Architects and engineers never talk about what buildings weigh. If they don't think about what buildings weigh, they certainly don't have any idea about performance per pound. The building industry is by far the most ignorant of all our activities.

I went to Harvard in 1913 and there was confronted by one of my older relatives. He said, "I've got to tell you some things, young man, that your father would have told you if he had lived. I am a very rich man, and I have learned something about our world that is not very nice." And he told me about Thomas Malthus and the fact that humanity was multiplying so much more rapidly than it was producing the goods to support itself. He told me then that it was not just me or the other fellow, but that there was really so little to go around that it would have to be me or one hundred others, and if I wanted to have a family of five that could grow and prosper, I would have to outdo five hundred others. You had to do it politely and in accordance with your own good conscience, but that was what you were up against.

I was very impressed by these ideas, but after my navy and building industry experiences, I began to suspect that there was a possibility that we might be able to do so much with so little that we might be able some day to take care of everybody. Therefore in 1927, I decided to take the initiative, and, without benefit of a patron, to investigate what would happen; what could happen, if world society or its industrial sectors were to apply the highest technology directly to making man a success on earth—not waiting for the new technology to first serve the weaponry and a generation later to upgrade the domestic arts in piecemeal fashion.

Proceeding in such a way could mean a high standard of living for all men on earth. But this will not be as a consequence of any political theory or its application by any political structure. When, twelve years ago, Eisenhower went to meet with Khrushchev in Geneva, both leaders had been informed by their military and scientific aids regarding the magnitude of the destructive capability of the atomic bomb. Eisenhower said, as he went to that conference, "there is no alternative to peace." I am sure that Khrushchev, with the same realization, must also have felt the terrible responsibility of that moment. Both men, being great political realists and hard-fact men, knew that they would not be able to make any important peace agreements conceived solely by themselves. They, as two men, could in no way alter the "balance of terror," as it is called. Their proposals and agreements, if any, would have to be backed up by their respective political parties. And their parties were always in mortal combat. At home, their chief opposition was waiting for altruistic moves from the "ins" as opportunities to impeach them for treachery to their respective sovereign power's ideological premises. Any soft-hearted step by the leader would throw his party out. While Eisenhower and Khrushchev couldn't yield an inch politically, ideologically, or militarily, both of them brought along their atomic scientists and allowed them to talk to each other discreetly through the curtain regarding peaceful uses of the atom. There was no formal statement made by these scientists. The newsmen gathered what they could.

Coincidental in time and place with this meeting in Geneva was a meeting of the food and agricultural organization of the United Nations. Coming clearly into scientific view and reported unequivocally by Gerard Piel, editor and publisher of the *Scientific American*, was the fact that for the first time in history it was a scientific possibility that the total resources of the earth, which now are serving only 40 per cent of humanity, could be made to serve 100 per cent by increasing resource performance per pound. The resources of the earth can be made not only to take care of 100 per cent of humanity instead of a minority, but can do so at an ever-improving standard of living, undreamt of by any sovereign to this date. For the first time in history, we knew that the world can be made to work. But this, of course, was frustrated completely by political barriers and political non-cooperation.

For twelve years, then, man has known that Malthus was wrong. And Malthus' viewpoint has been the basis of all political theory. The political theories have all been based on how to get along when there is not nearly enough for everyone. Karl Marx, as a great scholar studying in England, encountered the Malthusian data. It was very clear to Marx that there was not enough to go around. And Marx said, "Since there is not enough to go around for all and not even enough for 'many,' certainly those few who are arbitrarily favored by the prevailing system and thereby enabled to survive their allotted span of 'four score years and ten' ought to be the ones who are the most worthy." To Marx, those who do the work obviously are the most worthy.

Those who opposed him said that head work and daring enterprise which alone conceived of the great value to be realized by society could also increase abundance and support more people and the enterprisers should be conceded to be the exclusive few who could and should survive. Others said that it should be the bright ones, those who by their superior intellectual fitness alone could increase the numbers who could be supported. The choice of "who" should survive has always underlain all class warfare. Should it be the brightest, the toughest, or the bravest? And there are all kinds of in-between theories.

But let us get back to that young world wondering why the world isn't being made to work. Their intuitions are very keen and they have heard enough about the increase in capabilities from recent inventions to realize that more can be done with less. There has been very little discussion about that scientific confrontation at Geneva. I doubt that more than 1 per cent of humanity has ever read about it, although it forecast the possibility of a completely changed condition for man on earth. We talk about the prospects for humanity. We could today be a success. For the first time in history, I can say this and say it so it is understood. Industrialization has changed the whole picture of the future of man.

In the depths of the depression after 1929, when our big corporations were all shutting down, the Russians found gold, fur, and other trading capabilities. Stalin, working towards the success of all Russians, made contracts with the world's big corporations in England, Germany, France, and most importantly in the United States for the construction in Russia of prototype factories of all the different industrial activities. One reason why Khrushchev wanted to bury deep the memory of Stalin was that Stalin's purchase of the industrialization that made Russia successful robbed the communists of the possibility of accrediting that success to their political theory. Russia aspired to bless the world with absolute communism as the consequence of its earnest assumption that the validity of communism's politics was implied by Russia's half-century rise from abject poverty and illiteracy to co-supremacy in world military might. Russia acquired industrialization not under communist rule but under Stalin's absolute dictatorship, which enabled him to go outside his country and buy it. The historical fact is that industrialization, which is man's external metabolic processing, behaves just as man's internal metabolic processing from which internal functioning it directly derives. As with the internal functioning of man, industrialization functions under any color political system for any men, good, bad, wise or mad with equal metabolic efficiency.

Take from all of today's industrial nations all of their industrial machinery and all their energy-distribution networks and dump it into the ocean, and leave them all their ideologies, all their political leaders, and all their political organizations. A careful study has shown that within six months, two billion people will die of starvation, having gone through great pain and deprivation along the way.

However, if we leave the industrial countries with their present industrial machinery and their energy-distribution networks, and leave them also all the people who have routine jobs operating the industrial machinery and distributing its products without special initiative or innovation, and we take away from the industrial countries all their ideologies and all the politicians and political party workers and send them off by rocket ship to forever orbit the sun, the result will be that as many world people as now will keep right on eating, possibly getting on a little better than before. The political barriers will be down, there will be complete free world exchange of food, products, and services, and we could probably take care of many more people. These are the facts that confront us today.

I find then that the discontented young world is also used to the idea that the politician is somehow another parent, a fourth parent. And you go to the fourth parent, and you say, "Please, Mr. Fourth Parent, make the world work! I would like to have peace. I will have a sit-in or a strike until there is peace." They soon discover that the politician can't do anything because his last recourse is always war. He is always biased. He is always inherently appointed and has his authority coming only from one side. This side is invariably a small side. The mandates of the world's separate nationalized societies, acting exclusively through their respective national leaders, command the separate leaders to protect only their respective sovereign and unique positions. Even treaties with allies seeking mutual survival protection must be effected by the leaders' own initiative and be subject to ratification by the people or people's parliamentary representatives. The only spontaneously mandated authority the present political leader has is to channel the highest technology directly into weaponry systems' production to keep his nation in highest possible hitting-power advantage. So the young people are going to discover pretty soon that they are not going to get the politicians to make the world work.

It is a completely mistaken idea that politicians could ever make anything work. Up to the great crash, politicians were simply the local stooges of the great powers around the world. The great powers lost their control of the world in World War I when, in order for the in-powers to save themselves from the out-powers, they had to unleash the great Pandora's Box of the new technology. Ninety-nine per cent of the variable factors entering into control of all physical, industrial, and weaponry enterprise, as of World War I and immediately subsequent years, vanished from the sensorial ranges of the electro-magnetic frequency spectrum into the vastness of the infra and ultra sensorial physical-universes frequencies range of quantum physics, chemistry, and pure mathematics. As technology went from wire to wireless, from track to trackless, and from visible controls to invisible controls in general, the old masters' non-scientifically disciplined brains could not comprehend what was going on in the myriad of scientific specializations' invisible advances.

Paradoxically, it is to be remembered that in underwriting the new graduate schools of the universities, the great powers themselves had shortsightedly invented, designed, and underwritten specialization development. Bitter as it must have been to them to realize that they had organized their own undoing, the great powers thus became impotent in the prime design function of conceiving the evolutionary prime designs and comprehensive systems potentially to be realized from the new harvest of scientific specialization events. Specialization had been developed by the great, master world pirates as a means of dividing up all the bright ones, who might otherwise aspire to displace the great ones, and thus conquering society by keeping all powerful individuals compartmented by their specialization as the great master pirates reserved for themselves all the integrating of the wealth-producing potentials accruing to the specialists' multitude of special detail accomplishments. I call them the great pirates, for they were the masters of the world commerce which took place on the oceans covering three-quarters of the earth. Three miles off shore, all man-made laws were nil. Only the laws of the physical universe were operative. The great masters were, therefore, inherently "outlaws."

The year 1929 was the end of the great pirates' post-World War I attempt to recapture their controls. In 1929 the old masters died. The wheels of industry and commerce stopped. The world's people asked their political leaders to get them going again.

The people asked their political leaders to get the wheels going because the world's people, never having known of the invisible great pirates, believed that their political state heads, whom the grand masters invisibly manipulated, were the real comprehensive grand masters. The political leaders who had played their parts well looked secretly to their old masters for instruction on how to get the wheels going again and found that the old masters had disappeared they knew not where. Having waited as long as they dared for the reappearance of their old invisibly operating masters, who failed to show up, the world's major nations' respective political leaders took over. There was nothing else they could do.

The politicians, who had far less scientific competence than the old masters but who realized that protracted control of their newly realized power could only be maintained by the man who held the gun on the backs of the men who held the guns and that the men who held the guns had by training the ability to talk with the scientists, immediately passed the science-potentials-realizing problem over to their military establishments. My theory, then, is that man will not be able to get himself out of his troubles as long as he delegates to others the responsibility of making the world work.

In 1927, as I said earlier, I decided to investigate what would happen, if world society or its industrial sectors were to apply the highest technology directly to making man a success on earth.

There were no private, corporate, or governmental patrons with inherent need and mandate to underwrite my investigation. No government existed anywhere that said, "I will employ you and continually foster your attempt to make all world men successful exclusively through design science competence." No sovereign governments existed which represented more than a small percentage of "all" people. No corporations were interested in all men. There were, and are, no capitalized patrons, even amongst the the great foundations, chartered to underwrite such a comprehensive undertaking. I was convinced, however, that the proposition was worth investigating. Forsaking the a priori concept of "earning a living" I began the investigation in 1927 on my approximately zero capital, and wondered how I might organize myself to be effective.

How effective can the little individual be in the era of the massive corporation and the massive state? Is there anything that he can do that the massive corporation and the massive state can't do? The first thing he can do is—think. The corporation legally cannot think. Bureaucracy cannot think. It is just another name for offices. I was able to demonstrate within a fairly few years what the individual could do that the big corporation and the big state could not do in spite of seeming capital advantage.

For instance, I resolved, in my exploration of what an individual could do, never to spend any of my time trying to reform man. My philosophy and strategy confine my design initiative to reforming only the environment in contradistinction to the almost universal attempts of humans to reform and restrain other humans by political actions, laws, and codes. This restraining begins with the earliest parental attempts to reform their children's spontaneous behaviors in order to conform them to "accepted" standards and codes. The reforming of others is subsequently manifest in attempts of grownups to reform other grownups' patterns through politically enacted law.

Positive design science reformations of the environment must be undertaken with the intent of permitting man's innate faculties and facilities to be realized with subconscious coordinations of his organic process. Reform of the environment's purpose is to de-frustrate man's innate capabilities whether the frustration be by the physical environment or by the coordinated reflexes of other humans induced in those humans by the inadequacies of the environmental advantages as, for instance, mothers' unreasonable punishing of children, not for the children's direct act, but because of the mother's ever subconsciously present fear of the future, or of the all-history experienced approximately complete poverty which compounds the parent's drudge weariness and failure of the physical environment's providing any hope of the parent's opportunity to protect the new life inadvertently placed in their care.

Man as designed and invented is fantastically successful as an invention. Man as born is approximately perfect. One reason why humanity in general loves, admires, and worships human babies is that all physically normal babies are both unblemished and are designed to be physically successful. They are swiftly blemished by man's ignorantly served love. We hurt the new life, we doubt it, pinch it, and in great love but in great ignorance, we put it to continuingly greater disadvantage. We curtail its abilities. It is possible to design environments within which the child will be neither frustrated nor hurt yet free to develop spontaneously and fully without trespassing on others. If we design the environment properly, it will permit the child and man to develop safely and behave logically. The child has almost everything it needs right from birth. I hoped not to reform an older generation but to make it possible for a younger generation to grow up under much better conditions, so that it might be able to retain the capabilities with which it was born.

Growing directly out of my kind of experience came my interest in a new kind of transport unit. Because I had found it possible to do so much more with less in structures, I thought that the delivery of structures could be likewise advantaged. In the last fifteen years, more than three thousand of my structures have gone to fifty countries around the world, and the majority have been air delivered. This was the most economical means of delivery. There is no question about it. Those structures enclose space with clear spans and have the capability to withstand arctic snow loads, full hurricanes, and earthquakes. These enclosures are one-thousand-fold more economical weight-wise than the dome of St. Peter's in Rome and thirty times more efficient than equal clear spans in re-inforced concrete. They use an average of only 3 per cent of the weight of materials employed in an ordinary aluminum-structured building.

Finding that it was possible to do so much more with less in getting basic environment controlling gave me great hope that we might be able to do so much more with less that there would be enough for everybody. In the domestic world, nobody was working this way. I found that if I could deliver your home by air and if this building could take care of you on a completely autonomous basis with its machinery regenerating your energy processes, you would then be able to take as firm a position as an eagle does in some remote area where there is approximately no rental at all. But if a house is to be significantly autonomous, it must not be dependent on roads, railways, or even airplane landing strips. A dwelling which functions with maximum effectiveness wherever it is placed requires a family transport unit which really has the selective maneuverability of birds. It should be able to come in and go out by air or land and take off from a spot and in addition be capable of taxiing on land and water. So, in 1933, I went into initial programming to examine the possibility of an omni-directional, wingless, flying transport that could hover in the air, or could be directionally controlled by the jet blasts from gas turbines. The basic idea was locomotion on twin jet stilts, each directionally oriented and throttled as a discrete unit. This kind of flying pattern has now actually been demonstrated successfully. We will use it.

But in 1933, I went into the experiment of producing such a transport unit in order to test its ground taxiing qualities. When I taxied this device on the ground, people called it an automobile. There was no use in arguing, so I said that it was an automobile. It looked like a whale, a small whale—and Walter Chrysler became very interested in it and came out the following year with something called the Chrysler Air Flow car. Walter Chrysler asked if he could ride around in my transport unit and I took him around on a number of occasions. Then he asked me if I would take out his board of directors. Walter said, "This is the car that I wanted to build, but by the time my engineering department, sales department, the bank, and everyone else got through compromising our undertaking, it was neither a new car nor an old car; it wasn't anything." He said, "You have built the vehicle that I wanted to build. You happen to be very lucky; you have the right experience and the right concepts; and you have the capability to organize yourself to actually produce it." He said that our big corporations have checks and balances that keep a man from producing the wrong kind of inventions that might break up his company. These same checks and balances also guarantee that there won't be any kind of creative breakthrough.

The unique and superior advantage of the economic explorer mantaining his economic initiative in the face of the massive capital, staff, and equipment advantages of the large corporations and great states—who seemingly have top-heavy advantage—is demonstrated by the lone individual's complete freedom of the checks and balances of bureaucracy. Walter Chrysler found that I could produce three full-fledged operating prototypes of a better, more advanced automobile than could he and his Chrysler Corporation. My car had an aluminum body; his had a steel body. I had two Rolls-Royce body men, Polish sheet metal experts, Italian machine toolmen, and Scandinavian woodcraftsmen to assist me. I had a chrome-molybdenum, aircraft-steel chasis, one-eighth-inch aircraft shatterproof glass, and frames with dished lightening holes. I had front-wheel drive, rear engine and steering, and air-conditioning. My car was quite superior, and Walter said, "Your car is a superior device, so that it isn't really fair to compare costs, but let's see how it comes out." He went and got his costs. We found that my three prototypes cost me just one-quarter of what it cost the Chrysler Corporation to produce only one new prototype, and I was able to do it in one-third of the time.

I developed the geodesic structures entirely on my own initiative and economic momentum. I didn't have anyone telling me what to do. The Marine Corps and the United

States Navy came to me and said they needed to have advanced shelters which could be air deliverable. I was asked to come to Washington to make a contract for the development of their structures, but I said that I would not go near Washington. That was one thing that I had learned not to do. If you want to see what an individual can do, don't waste your time in Washington. I said that I have already developed my structures, which was the real reason that they had contacted me; I already have my patents and if they would like to use some of them, just come around and use those that I shall let them have. So the commandant of the Marine Corps ordered the head of aviation logistics to take office with me wherever I was—I was visiting a number of universities at that time. A big fat report was made and sent into the Marine Corps by the head of aviation logistics which said that I had the first advance in mobile shelters in the past twenty-six hundred years. The report showed that I was able, time and again, to produce satisfactory, working, structural innovation prototypes in one month with an average of only five thousand dollars of my own money and with the help of thirty university students and the results were superior in every way to those obtained by the Navy department and the Marine Corps dealing exclusively with prime industrial contractors whose projects average two years and cost a quarter of a million dollars. Often their methods failed to produce even satisfactory results. Quite clearly the individual initiative is at highest advantage with the least staff and property.

It is common thinking to assume that progress can be accomplished only through powerful political or economic mandate. This is overlooking the far vaster prerogative of the inventor. The inventor's personal initiative has natural and immediate access to all the potentials of the universe.

Edison, Bell, Marconi, and the Wright brothers needed no licenses from anyone to light the night, to shrink the earth, and to interlink all of humanity. Inventors pay no attention to man-made laws. They obey only the natural, physical law which alone governs what man may ultimately do to make himself a success. If humanity succeeds in becoming a total success, it will have been initiated by the Wright and Bell type inventions and not by the always debilitating and often lethal biases of politics.

Inventions occur when individuals, frustrated by circumstance, eschew negative blaming and undertake positive physical environment reforms rather than abstract human reforms. The latter depend precariously upon moral, ethical, and legal codes which are enforceable only by the application of negative penalties. The independent, physical environment reforming inventions have integrated, figuratively speaking, as streamliningly divided, double-decked, banked, and clover-leafed lifeways of human behaviors. These lifeways will permit ever-increasing numbers of humans to survive logically and sense-satisfyingly without mutually frustrating interferences.

Revolution by design and invention is the only revolution tolerable to all men, all societies, and all political systems everywhere. Every nation welcomed the invention of the airplane and of refrigeration. Every nation welcomed and employed the transistor. All will welcome economically feasible desalinization. There is a dawning awareness on the part of the young world that it can begin to take the initiative for a design and invention revolution. Initiative springs only from within the individual: it can neither be delegated nor created. It can be vacated. Initiative can only be taken by the individual on behalf of his own self-conviction of the necessity to overcome his conditioned reflexes which have accustomed him theretofore always to yield authority to the wisdom of others. Initiative is only innate and is highly perishable.

It is my own working hypothesis, my prophecy, right now, that the young world is about to take the initiative as inventor-scientist and, using those facilities in universities immediately available to them, will succeed in converting the resources available to us to such a high degree of effectiveness as to take care of 100 per cent of humanity and so ensure the success of man.

Engineers, architects, scientists in general, are all slaves: they are all operating in slave professions. They cannot take a design or inventor initiative. They can only go to work when they are put to work by a client. And they only go to work on what the client wants to have done, so that, in reality, the client is the prime designer, the initiator. The great powers that I have mentioned, while they existed, used to be prime designers. They deliberately kept their professionals under control and they themselves integrated the new-found potentials and they alone conceived what they would do with the totality. They were the comprehensivists and great integrators.

Long ago the medical profession was also a slave profession and then the doctors broke away from slavery. It happened as follows: the Pharaoh said to the doctor, "Doctor, give me that pink stuff." The doctor ventured, "Pharaoh, I think the pink stuff is the wrong stuff." The Pharaoh said, "Give me the pink stuff!!" The doctor did. They put the living doctor in the tomb with the dead Pharaoh.

Doctors found that they were only called in when a client was in a critical condition. Doctors were also often involved in contagious diseases and epidemics. Doctors have always been in critical proximity to death. They naturally wanted to get out from the miserable position of always conceding to the ignorance of the client. So about two thousand years ago, the doctors developed a vast conspiracy. They said to one another, "we see that there are more clients than we shall ever need. Therefore, we do not have to compete for clients. Therefore, we can pool our strategic information, our experience, and our efforts." By pooling their information, they were able to discover the otherwise invisible patterns of recurring epidemics and the probable location and complex sources of infection as well as preventatives and other cures.

The medics said, "we must become as anticipatory as possible in our conspiracy, for the earlier we get a case, the better our opportunity of mastering it. Therefore, we shall organize our profession on the assumption that sooner or later every part and process of the human organism is going to be in trouble. Therefore, the earlier we know about every part and process of which a human consists, the better prepared we shall be when the inevitable troubles occur."

So the medical scientists themselves established a comprehensive system for exploring and anticipating. The doctors also said, "we must have client cooperation. Therefore, we shall listen to his nonsensical diagnosis and congratulate him on being such a good and illuminating patient, but we shall then write out our prescription in a secret language known only to us." Later on, the great powers realized that by these means, the doctors had won freedom for themselves and their profession. The doctors had really become very, very powerful. But the great powers were sometimes very old and very tired and wanted to enjoy in comfort their declining years, and they knew that they could be helped in this by the doctors. So the great powers let the doctors keep their freedom.

The doctors became so powerful that they could have taken over the world. They consulted among themselves as to whether they were really interested in being great rulers or whether they were really interested in man's physical success. They really were inspired by man; their curiosity was really fired by the internal organic processes of humanity. They were the first profession to resolve together to take an oath of responsibility to human society. All the other professions have remained in slavery, although the real reasons for their original enslavement, the great powers, no longer exist.

It is possible—and it is going to be necessary if society is to continue on earth—for the professional scientists, engineers, and architects to satisfactorily anticipate the economic needs of not only the next generation of humanity, but of all generations of all men to come. It is going to be necessary for the scientists, engineers, and professionals in general, and the world students in particular, to take the initiative in respect to articulating the total advantages to make the world work for all.

The engineers, scientists, and artists, supported by the young world working within the framework of advanced education facilities, are going to have to take the initiative in bringing to full success the social-support function of world industrialization, which consists of all the externalized, metabolically regenerating organics of man—just as did the medical scientists two thousand years ago in taking the initiative away from their clients in respect to repairing any unsuccessful functioning of the clients' (the public's) internal metabolic regeneration organisms.

Every invention is an externalization of originally integral functions of humanity. Man invents a cup because he needs his hands for various other purposes than drinking with them. He can't run around with water in his hands without spilling it. But in inventing the cup, he invented a container that could handle much hotter liquids than his hands could handle. Acid liquids further externalized this function until finally man began to break through to new performing capabilities for his tools. Industrialization consists of tools. I define industrialization as the extra corporeal, organic, metabolic regeneration of humanity. Industrialization is completely organic and inter-related. Industrialization must be recognized and operated on a total world and total humanity basis or it is nothing. Industrialization involves all the resources of the earth, all the knowledge and all the experience of all men everywhere, and involves everybody on earth as the logical clients to be advantaged by the total integrated capability.

I am not talking about the architects, engineers, or scientists becoming politicians. The doctors did not have to take over the world and run the post offices in order to be able to satisfactorily anticipate man's internal bodily needs. All they had to do was go to work amongst themselves to find out what the physical tasks were that they had to perform for any and all of humanity to free them from afflictions. But when you are a practicing professional, you have very little money with which to deal and you cannot reorganize society. I suggest to the scientists, engineers, and architects to operate as visiting committees to change the educational curricula requirements for professional degrees. Students should be permitted to organize themselves in engineering-architectural science to study total world industrialization. The young world must have the opportunity to employ this knowledge to make their world work. It is perfectly possible to have as part of the qualified professional degree, engineers, architects, and scientists joining together to deal with the external organics of man as the medical men did with the internal organics of man and thereby undertaking the anticipation of the various ways of doing more with less in order to up performance to take care of 100 per cent of humanity.

What are the tasks necessary to make 100 per cent of humanity a success: how can we do so without ever advantaging one human at the expense of another? What are the resources? Consisting mostly of recirculating scrapped metals, 80 per cent of all the metals that have ever been mined are still at work. And all these metals are now occupied in structures and machinery which operating at full capacity can take care of only 44 per cent of humanity: that is, they can take care of 4 per cent more than are now being taken care of. During this twentieth century, the combined amounts of scrap and newly mined metals per each world man have been continually decreasing because population is increasing faster than the discovery of new ore resources. For man to go from less than 1 per cent in 1900 to 40 per cent of humanity enjoying a high standard of living today—despite decreasing resources—cannot be explained by anything other than doing more with less.

If humanity understood that the real world problem is that of upping the performances per pound of the world's metals and other resources, we might attempt to solve the problem deliberately, directly, and efficiently. It should be a world around the university students' elective research undertaking. Doing more with less can be very greatly accelerated. This is particularly evident if we look into the overall mechanical efficiencies as now operatively employed. Various kinds of engines have contrasting relative efficiencies as to how much work they can deliver out of the energies they consume. An automobile's reciprocating engine is only about 15 per cent efficient. The new gas turbines are 30 per cent, coal-burning turbo-electric generators are 40 per cent, jet engines are about 60, and some of the new fuel cells have efficiencies of 80 per cent. The world's total operating economy is today operating at an appallingly low overall mechanical efficiency level in which the machines realize, in energy work done, only one twenty-fifth—i.e:. 4 per cent of the potential of the thus wastefully consumed energy. To increase the overall efficiency to only 12 per cent could take care of all humanity. But the necessary great network of world industrialization needed for such an increase in efficiencies is completely frustrated by all existing political barriers. I say, then, here are the prospects for humanity. The prospects are that man can make life a success for all men. And there are excellent prospects because the new young world is the most literate in world history and with all its training and knowledge is the first generation to think entirely as world man.

I use the word "synergy" to show experimentally the behavior of whole systems unpredicted by behavior of the parts. The known behavior of the whole and the known behavior of some of the parts (at least three) make possible discovery of the required behavior of the other parts. I assume that all planning of humanity's economic, urban, industrialization, and other undertakings must start with world trendings and possible modifications of the total or world environment.

According to my speculative reconstruction, the ecological history of humanity around the planet earth has two chapters. In chapter one, humanity, whose bodies are 90 per cent water, lived in huts on rafts beside the rivers, lakes, bays, and oceans, for fish were the most plentiful food and the raft kept the humans safe from the wild animals on the shore. Some of these raft dwellers were blown out to sea and preponderantly eastward around earth's surface, three quarters of which is water. In the second chapter of all history, men learned to sail windward. Following the sun, to which they intuitively attributed their metabolic regeneration, men worked westward fighting into the head-wind seas. In Japan, that originally sea-faring people have an annual "Golden Boy Day." They celebrate by flying fish-shaped kites above the roofs of their homes; one for each of their male children. The kites symbolize the salmon, who swims and leaps upstream in order to regenerate. That is the Japanese ideal.

Approximately the whole of the last ten thousand years' span of recorded history takes place during chapter two's preponderantly westbound movement of humanity. In the Eurasian continent, where 76 per cent of humanity exists, this westward motion finally funnels into Western Europe. As humanity converged, it crossbred. Western Europe represented an amalgam of a myriad of previously isolated "nations." The "nations" had developed through millenniums of inland, inbred adaptions to local subsistence patterns. Along the waterfronts, the sailors crossbred.

Crossbreeding Europeans, intermingling with Angles and Jutes, poured into the British Isles to crossbreed even more. Westbound Indian Ocean people inhabited Africa in ever further westward, tribally inbreeding, inland isolations. Then crossbreeding western European humanity jumped westward across the Atlantic to the Americas. For ten successive generations, they have settled further westward. As they moved westward they yet accelerated their crossbreeding, not only with their own, westbound, chapter two Eurasian stocks but also with the Eurasian stock of chapter one, which had drifted eastward to the American continent at least ten thousand years earlier. Into the North and South American continents and their islands there also flowed westward, both by slave trade and migration, a swiftly crossbreeding homogenization of the inbred African tribesmen.

In California, at the mid-point of the western shores of America, crossbreeding man has already become so genetically integrated as to defy superficial identification with any of the earlier inbred national characteristics of Eurasia. In California, today, we find an advanced phase of crossbred world man poised on an epochal springboard about to fly both skyward and into the seas' depths around the earth, thus to open chapter three of history. In logical consequence of this historical trending the United Nations was born on the west coast of America a score of years ago. Logically, the air and space vehicles of man's acceleration into world and universe citizenship are predominantly produced on the west coast of America. California is the center of the outermost jump-off pad of humanity's springboard. From this pad, humanity is taking off from its flounder-, snail-, and crablike existence only around the two dimensional bottom of the sky-ocean world into its self-interference free, four-dimensional occupancy of universe. Chapter three of humanity's history will be written in terms of world man becoming conscious of his total potentials.

Ninety-nine per cent of all the search, research, and development as well as of all the operating controls of man's entry into the one-town world and its surrounding sky-ocean is conducted exclusively in the ranges of the electromagnetic spectrum that are infra and ultra to man's sensorial apprehending. Only through mind-conceived and brain-operated instruments does humanity command the operations of its birth and entry into world and universe citizenship. Education is therefore essential and central to man's successful transformation.

I was asked to give the quarterly address to the faculty at Massachusetts Institute of Technology in the winter of 1950. I stood up, and, because I hadn't prepared anything, found myself thinking out loud—something that surprised me very much. I said that I was surprised to be invited to speak to them because they were all so ignorant. They looked astonished, and I was a little astonished myself. So I had to explain why I thought they were ignorant. And I said that all of them as scientists, on leaving M.I.T., went home to their families, and on a beautiful summer evening said to their wives, or daughters, or sweethearts, "darling, look at that beautiful sunset." And all the scientists realistically saw and as yet "see" the sun setting—"going down."

I wouldn't think much about this "seeing" of the sun "setting" by a taxi driver or other layman, but, I said, "as scientists, you have had five hundred years since Copernicus and Galileo to get your senses in gear with your own experimentally-proven information. You know that the sun is not setting. You know that the earth is revolving to obscure the sun, but you 'see' the sun 'set.' Because it is taking more than five hundred years to get mentally in gear with your own theory, it must be because you don't know how and probably haven't even tried: therefore, I think you are fundamentally ignorant." Actually, their fault is caused by bad reflex conditioning. There is often an additional special blockage that hinders grown people regarding sun relationships, which is the poetical sound of "sunset." No one has invented a more poetical single word to express being revolved out of sight of the sun. Which way we see depends on what we are told at the outset of life before we unconsciously, or subconsciously, lock together our spontaneous brain reflexes.

I found it possible at forty years of age to correct my erroneous "sunset" reflexes. It took much time, however.

Therefore, I know that we can say that it is not impossible to recondition our adult reflexes, but the later, the more difficult. I find that the scientists are experimentally remiss in continuing to yield to feelings that do not agree with their theories. They have failed because of ignorance, or laziness, or fear of being "different," to bring whatever they have learned of the universe into correct conceptional realizations by the child. They haven't taken the trouble to test the theory they have acquired, so they carefully continue to misinform the children. They are apparently ignorant of the fact that the child can most easily learn to see things correctly only if he is spoken to intelligently right from the beginning. "Intelligently" means thinking things through to discover the need for experimental preciseness plus the disciplining of the self to do so. I think that it is unscientific of the scientists in the educational processes to let these matters ride, and to go on debilitating whole new generations one after another of billions of young, who, if geared sensorially with correct theory, might have effective common sense enough to make the world work.

I note that the scientists also use the words "up" and "down" hundreds of times daily. So, I asked the M.I.T. faculty if any of them could tell me the part of universe that is "up." Are the people in China upside down? Those deeply in-conditioned words "up" and "down" are derived from the millenniums in which man thought erroneously of his universe as a horizontal island, as "the four corners of the earth," and as the "wide, wide world" in an infinitely extended horizontal ocean with an obvious "up" and "down" set of parallel perpendiculars to his flat plane—heaven up and hell down. Whatever other dimensional relationships could there be to an infinitely extended "flat" plane? Though as yet difficult to purge from yesterday's reflex-conditioned, flat-earth concepts and speech, to man far out in universe the sphericity of earth becomes evident and "up" and "down" soon become meaningless. But the clipper ship captains of the last century sailing their ships around the world and the aviators flying planes around to China in this century discovered that they didn't have to turn their ships upside down when they reached China. Aviators have discarded the words "up" and "down." Now they come "in" for landings and they go "out." Astronauts come "in" with respect to various specific bodies in the universe and they go "out" from them. "In" is individually unique as a direction toward the center of any one system—but "out" is common to them all. There is no shape of space—only omni-directional non-conceptional "out" and the specifically directional conceptual "ins." "Space" has no identifiable meaning. The atmosphere's molecules are forever shifting position. The stars overhead now are underfoot twelve hours later. The stars themselves are swiftly moving in respect to one another. Many of them have not been where you now see them for millions of years; many burnt out long ago. The sun's light takes eight seconds to reach us. When you see the sun tangent to the western horizon, you are seeing around the horizon. And the light of the brightest star in the heaven takes four and a quarter million years to get to us and that star probably burnt out a million years ago. "Space" is meaningless. We have relationships, but not space.

I went on to say to the M.I.T. faculty: "As scientists, you tell me that the wind is blowing from the northwest, which implies that you can really blow air great distances and that there is really some place called 'northwest,' which of course, there isn't." Air cannot be blown great distances. It curves back upon itself in evoluting-involuting doughnut-shaped ring clouds—from tobacco smoke-ring size to the atomic bomb's mushroom-ring size. An electric fan at the front door cannot push air through all the rooms of the house, but it can pull air through all the windows and through the rooms around corners and out through the front door. Whereas pushed air cannot travel great distances, pulled air tries to straighten out and can be pulled over enormous distances. What the scientists really mean when they say it is blowing from the northwest is that there is a low pressure to the southeast of us which is sucking the air from all directions and pulling it past us as we happen to be situated on earth northwestward of the low pressure area. So why don't the scientists say, "a low pressure southeast of us is sucking" or simpler yet, "southeast's sucking"?

At any rate, I was able to get the M.I.T. scientists to laugh at themselves, realizing that they were reflexedly "ignorant." They are as yet ignorant because they have not yet learned by experimentally proven means how to gear many of their theories to their sensorial capabilities. How can they make sense if their senses deny their theory? They try to excuse themselves by saying that science deals now primarily with sub-visible, sub-audible, sub-smellable, sub-touchable phenomena. But it is possible, through the use of generalized scientific principles, abstract and independent of size, to make special case conceptional models at sense-apprehendable sizes of all phenomena. The fact is, that scientists, like aviators flying in fog at night, went "on instruments" in the mid-nineteenth century. There is today a greater gap between the scientist as a scientist and the same scientist as a human being than the gap between the scientists and the non-science-educated members of the human family. In contradistinction to the esteem in which world society holds them, scientists are the most confused and irresponsible human beings now alive. They are like hens laying scientific "eggs" which businessmen sell to politicians to be scrambled, easied over, or dropped as we hurtle toward oblivion. If our lives are left only to their care, we may soon be destroyed.

Not only do I find that the scientists at M.I.T. and everywhere else around the world are out of gear with their own theory (as once was I, to a far worse degree), but, I find, also by actual experience, that many if not most of the axioms of our would-be-simplest geometry and arithmetic are faulty. Axioms are defined by Webster as "statements which need no proof because their truth is obvious." Because they take axioms erroneously as obvious (as with the sun "setting"), "pure" mathematicians deliberately sidestep the experimentally developed basis of all physical science. Much of mathematics deals with phenomena which hold true only if their axioms are proven experimentally valid. Because experiment invalidates most of the axioms of mathematics such as the existence of solids, continuous surfaces, straight lines, etc., much of the mathematical curricula sanctioned by mathematical educators, adopted by school boards, and taught in all elementary schools is false, irrelevant, discouraging, and dibilitating to the children's brain functioning. Science is culpable for allowing this process to continue. Sense-illiterate scientists haven't taken the trouble to find out how to stop each generation from relaying to the next one disciplines that are misleading and frustrating.

Obviously one of the reasons why scientific education has seemed too difficult for many is the fact that much of its mathematics is founded upon experimentally unprovable myths which must greatly offend the intuitive sensitivity of the lucidly thinking young life. I find it shocking that I can recite to you many mathematical fallacies that we may be fated to go on teaching for another decade, thus to ruin the extraordinary learning potential of another whole generation. All of this mischief of irresponsibility of the so-called grownups will have to be undone, probably at painful cost to world society, quite possible at total cost. We don't have much time to couple both our theories and our senses with mathematical and physical reality, thereby to gain universally spontaneous cooperation in tuning man's competence first to have himself and then to make himself a success in universe.

Since 1932, mathematical-physicists, physicists, chemists, and many other scientists have been through one house cleaning after another. In contradistinction "pure" mathematics and all the branches of the "pure" variety that permeate academic disciplining, on the pretext that it is pure—ergo transcendental to applied or experimental reality—have failed to purge themselves of unproven axiomatic conceptions, adopted almost entirely in the millenniums before present experimental science began to alter man's comprehensive ecology and cognitive capabilities.

In 1917, I found myself asserting that I didn't think that nature had a department of mathematics, a department of physics, and a department of biology and had to have meetings of department heads in order to decide what to do when you drop a stone in the water. Universe, i.e., nature, obviously knows just what to do, and everything seemed beautifully coordinated. Everything went smoothly, sublimely. So, I thought that nature probably had one coordinate system and that that system would be the most economical, arithmetical, and geometrical system with which to interaccount all transactions and transformations. I thought that it was preposterous when I was told that real models were not employed in advanced science, because science was able to deal with nature by use of completely unmodelable mathematical abstractions. I could not credit that universe suddenly went abstract at some micro-level of investigation, wherefor in order to be able to deal with the physical universe in the most advanced stages of frontiering one had to deal entirely with abstract formulae, unmodelable mathematics. As we acquired larger microscopes and larger telescopes, I found that models always showed up. And men, satisfied with their abstract preoccupations, didn't bother or didn't seem to know how to explain the emerging pictures of the obviously systematic but strange, often asymmetrical, but sometimes symmetrical models. I thought then that if we could find nature's own coordinate system, we would understand the models and we would be able to develop much higher exploratory and application capability. In chemistry, atoms were associating and disassociating in beautiful, whole, simple-number arrangements, such as H_2O. Chemistry seemed to avoid irrational fractions. Everything was accountable in simple and whole numbers. I felt that if we ever found nature's coordinate system, it would be very simple and always rational.

I am confident now that I have found that coordinate system because I have submitted it to bodies of competent scientists. In October, 1965, I met with competent scientists of all the related fields of physics. I made comprehensive disclosure of the ramifications of the coordinate system which I have discovered and explored for more than a third of a century. They accepted the coordinate system which I disclosed as probably being nature's most efficient means of accounting nature's generalized relationships.

The omni-rational coordinate system which I have named *synergetics* is not an invention. It is purely discovery. I am quite confident that with the complete and simple modelability of synergetics, it will be possible for children at home receiving closed-circuit television documentaries and making their own models to do valid nuclear physics formulations at kindergarten age. With fundamental structuring experience and sense perception models, children will be making experiments that discover why water does what it does. They will really understand what a triangle is and what it can do and does. The obsoleting educational system taught people to think in "squares" and to measure in terms of inches, squares, and cubes. We've come to assume that a cubical or rectilinear house has structural integrity. If you make a cube with little sticks and rubber joints, you'll find that cubes always collapse. They have no structural integrity whatsoever. We find ourselves starting out on all the wrong axiomatic bases. When we use tetra-hedra to account nature we are three times more efficient (with energy) than when we account in cubes. And nature is always most efficient.

I have stressed that where men think of themselves as most scientifically advanced, they are sometimes dealing in axioms that no longer hold true. What they are doing does hold true in relation to those false axioms. But inasmuch as they didn't start with axioms disclosed experimentally by nature they are dealing with non-universe, and are playing perfectly good games, and I love them for doing it, but they are playing games that are completely irrelevant to what we and nature are doing and need to do.

We are always told in both Euclidean and non-Euclidean geometries that a plurality of lines can be run through any one point. The engineer puts a point on a paper and draws line after line (approximately) through (approximately) the same point. He asumes this to be theoretically and realistically done. But try this with knitting needles or even the thinnest line elements you can find. In fact, reduce your line to the size of a neutron's diameter. Let your "line" be the trajectory in the cloud chamber of a neutron shot into a plurality of atoms. Suddenly there is an inter-ference of the trajectory as the neutron interferes with another nuclear component's linear trajectory and the component separates into further subcomponents as all of the individual atomic components now diverge angularly from one another in identifiable angular directions unique to each, having failed to permit the neutrons' simultaneous passage through the one point of interference. Because they cannot go through the same point at the same time, we get little angles by which cloud-chamber physicists recognize the subatomic particles. If lines, which experimentally are always vectors, are unable to go simultaneously through the same point, then we can't have "planes" which are absurdly thin wafers of solids. We find that we are dealing with a very different kind of universe from the one that we are told about and that the children still are "learning" about in grade schools.

Because you can't have two actions going through the same point at the same time, we have the phenomenon of reflection, with which we are all familiar, or we have refraction. These two experimentally reliable interference phenomena are direct consequences of the fact that actions cannot take place through the same point at the same time.

Mathematically, there are very important concepts regarding the tetrahedron. The tetrahedron is made up of four triangles. The angles of each triangle are inter-stabilized. Each of the separate angles, which as such were originally amorphous—that is, unstable, becomes stable because the vector (line) opposite any angle of any triangle is always operating at and between the ends of the levers which are the sides of the angle, thus providing maximum advantage over its own angular stability with minimum effort. The triangle is the fundamental function of structure, but it always takes two functions, the positive and negative, to make any structure. The tetrahedron is the simplest structure known to man. The triangle exists operationally only as a positive or negative function of a

polyhedron. Of all the polygons, only triangles are struc-
turally stable. A square, as I said earlier, folds up. Try any
other rubber-jointed polygon: it will fold up. Try a rubber-
jointed triangle: it won't fold up: it is stable. If we want
to have a structure, we have to have triangles, and to have
a structure requires a minimum of four triangles. A structural system may be symmetrical or asymmetrical, but it
always has within-ness and without-ness. A structure or
system divides universe into two parts; all of the universe
that is inside the structure or system and all the rest of
universe that is outside the structure or system. We find
that there are only three types of fundamental omni-tri-
angular, symmetrical structural systems. We can have three
triangles around each vertex of a symmetrical structure,
making a regular tetrahedron. We can have four triangles
around each vertex of a symmetrical structure, making a
regular octahedron. Finally, we can have five triangles
around each vertex of a symmetrical structure, making the
regular icosahedron. The tetrahedron, octahedron, and
icosahedron are made up, respectively, of one, two, and five
pairs of positive-negative function open triangles. We can't
have six symmetrical or equilateral triangles around each
vertex because the sum of the angles would be six times
sixty degrees, or three hundred and sixty degrees, thus
forming an infinite edgeless plane. The structural system
with six equilateral triangles around each vertex never comes
back upon itself. It cannot be constructed with pairs of
positive-negative function open triangles. A structural system must return upon itself in all directions. If the system's openings are all triangulated, it is structured with
minimum effort. There are only three possible omni-sym-
metrical, omni-triangulated, least-effort structural systems
in nature: the tetrahedron, octahedron, and icosahedron.
When their edges are all equal in length, the volumes of

these three structures are approximately and respectively: one, four, and eighteen and two-thirds.

When I began to explore the volume relationships above and gave the simplest, the tetrahedron, a volume value of one, I found that a cube had a volume of exactly three. That's very interesting because if you try to account in cubes for nature's energy associabilities as structural systems, you use up three times as much space as you do if you count space volumes in tetrahedronal units. The physicists have found that nature only uses those structures which are most economical: therefore, she should not use cubes to quantitate her structurings. Cubes, as you know, represent our x, y, z coordinate system.

If you use tetrahedra as your coordinating system, something very fundamental and economical happens. A cube's angles are each ninety degrees. When you want to make a bigger cube out of littler cubes—want to double the size of the cube—you must put eight little cubes together symmetrically "closest stacked" around one point. The edges of the thus created big cube are each two units of little cube-edge long. The big cube edges are two. The face areas are four. The volume of the two linear-module edged cube is eight, which is the third power of two.

When we deal in tetrahedra, we are dealing with sixty degree angle systems, since in a regular tetrahedron all of the angles are sixty degrees: they are equilateral (and equiangular) triangles. Heretofore when the scientists found an energy relationship in the fourth power value, they were unable to make a conceptional model of it because there is no fourth perpendicular to a cube which is not in a plane parallel to one of the planes of the cube. But the scientists did not need a model to calculate fourth power problems. They were able to handle it very easily algebraically. They did it by using what they called an imaginary number, e.g., by using the square root of minus one. If that sounds complex, don't let it bother you. What they were saying was that, in effect, they had a cubical clock. Their cubical day consisted of eight little cubes around the center of the big cube. The first dimension used up one cube, the second dimension used up four cubes, and the third dimension used up all eight cubes. Their day's entire clock capacity would only take care of three dimensions. So what they did was to borrow cubes from "tomorrow" or from "yesterday." They then carried out their problem algebraically without any reference to conceptional models. After they got finished, they paid back the borrowed time and once again had a visual three-dimensional model quantity.

When sixty degrees is used for coordination, imaginary or complex numbers are not needed to carry out fourth-power calculations because there is a volume of twenty tetrahedra around one point instead of eight. Two to the fourth power is sixteen and there are twenty tetrahedra with which to work. The additional two to the second power in the model is very useful when this vectorial grouping around a common nucleus is employed to account for nuclear energy behaviors. When the nuclear group of vectors has a radial or edge module of two (as do the eight small cubes in closest packing), then the vectorial system has a volume around its center of one hundred and sixty, which is five times two to the fifth power. It is perfectly possible then, today, for a child to make fourth- and fifth-power models with tetrahedronal and octahedronal building blocks. Einstein was working on fifth-power problems just before his death. He was trying to reconcile gravity and electromagnetics.

I have found this arithmetical-geometrical energy co-ordinating system to coincide rationally and comprehensively with nature's behaviors. With this system, models can be made that can handle fourth- and fifth-power problems. Systems on an x-y-z coordinating systems using cubes cannot do this. This latter fact has accounted for the discard of models and the preoccupation of science with a completely abstract treatment of nature.

Linus Pauling received his first Nobel Prize for his contributions to the general knowledge of chemical structures. He gave me his Nobel Laureate paper to read and it was the best and most concise history of chemical structures that I know. The first part of the paper is about organic chemistry.

It was in the years around 1800 that the organic chemists, while making experiments, discovered that the associating-disassociating in organic chemistry seemed to be in whole number increments of one, two, three, four. Those were the only numbers that had to be accounted for in all organic chemistry experiments. In about 1810, a man named Frankland was the first to make a written notation of this fact. Then two men, Kekule and Cooper, added a little more to the same information. In 1835, a Russian, Butlerov, was the first to use the term "chemical structure." He was the first to say that one, two, three, four seemed to have something to do with "bonding" together, and he called this bonding "valence." Then there was a gap in further fundamental discovery until 1885, when a man named Vant Hof said that the oneness, twoness, threeness, and fourness were the four vertexes of a tetrahedron. Other chemists looked at him askance. He was called an outright charlatan and a faker of every kind. Otherwise, the other chemists paid no attention to Vant Hof's research. He was greatly stunned but still continued his experiments. He lived long enough to give experimental, optical proof of the tetrahedronal configuration of carbon, the combining master of organic chemistry. Vant Hof was the first chemist to receive the Nobel Prize. From this time on, chemistry recognized that organic chemistry was coordinated tetrahedronally.

Two tetrahedra linked together by one vertex of each is a single bonding and is very flexible. Bonding by one vertex is like a universal joint and is a gas situation. Many tetrahedra so linked could be stretched to fill more space than if linked mutually by two or three vertexes. Two bonds form a hinge along one edge of two tetrahedra. This is still a flexible situation as in liquids, but it is, of course, much more compact. Triple bonding or face bond between two tetrahedra is rigid as in crystals. You can get four vertexes of tetrahedra together, which means that they will be congruent and most densely compacted, possibly like diamonds.

In Vant Hof's day, the majority of the chemists were metallurgists, and they had found no vertexial bondings. That was probably the reason that they became incensed at Vant Hof's hypothesis. Although there exist in nature visible crystals with the forms of octahedra, rhombic dodecahedra, etc., the other chemists found no way to account for their atomic structuring. In 1932, approximately half a century after Vant Hof, Linus Pauling began to use X-ray diffraction machines to probe metal structures. X-ray diffraction machines operate in ways analogous to radar: X-ray diffraction sends x-rays right into the atoms to be explored, which rays are bounced back giving general pattern information that can be interpreted. In this way, Pauling discovered all the metals he analyzed to be tetrahedronally coordinate, but instead of being linked vertex to vertex, they were linked mid-edge to mid-edge, often with common centers of gravity. While Linus Pauling has not, to my knowledge, said that all metals are tetrahedronally coordinated, so far no exceptions have been called to my attention.

Pauling's Nobel Laureate discourse twenty years ago discussed no exceptions.

For eighty years, organic chemistry has recognized tetrahedronal coordination. Twenty years of x-ray diffraction experiments has found the metals tetrahedronally coordinate. I came to this subject in an entirely different way from that of the chemists and have found the tetrahedron to be the coordinating unit in experimental mathematics, which is what the scientists call my work. I will say to you what I have said to C. P. Snow: "All of nature's formulating is tetrahedronally coordinate." And Snow, a scientist, said, "From what you have related to me, I am inclined to agree with you. In fact, this information comes to me at a very strategic moment in my life." In the 1965 New Year statements harvested by the press from world leaders, Lord Snow had quite a long piece saying that he was able to retract his "two forever unjoinable worlds" (science and the humanities) statements. He felt that he was wrong and it looked like the chasm between the two were closing. In the nineteenth century, the literary man had the models taken away from him. He had no model to explain science to the people. Popularization of science employed superficial romance. True science was shunned as too difficult, too dry, or too obscure. Now the bridge has been found between structural conceptuality and pure science exploration.

As conceptuality returns, the great chasm between the humanities and the sciences will be completely repaired. The power of man's thinking, his ability to deal with his universe in ways which differ completely from yesterday, will no longer be frustrated by a lack of conceptional formulation. Man will be able to handle problems with numbers. He will read calculus and advanced mathematics: he will know what science is doing. In the next decade, you will find nuclear physics models in the kindergartens. My prospects for humanity, then, are favorable. I see that the young world is intent on taking over and using its complete coordinating capabilities all around the world and also being as logical as human beings need to be in coordinating with one another. They will not need governments or limiting rules. There will be cooperative action of the young people around the world to tackle the problems of how to do more with ever less to make the world work for 100 per cent of humanity. I think the prospects for man are very high.

COMMENTARIES

BLAKESLEE: Yesterday at lunch Mr. Fuller was telling me of a book that he is writing on speculative anthropology, as to how man may have come about forming our society. One point he makes is that man began living by the sea on a raft near the shore; this kept him away from the big cats and other animals he didn't want to encounter. Another of his ideas was that a boat became our first form of locomotion, long before the wheel.

I have my own speculation on this score, which is more naïve. I see the first group of humans standing out in the open. It is raining. They are cold and miserable. Then one member of this group begins to reason, and he thinks, well, if we went inside this cave we would be out of this mess. And so they do that and there is great cheering by all his friends because a scientist has been born. It's a Bucky Fuller who has come along with an idea. But they are still cold, and so somebody else gets stimulated. He noticed that lightning set a fire when he was out in the forest, and when he got near the fire he became warm, and so he took some wood and fire into the cave. This too was greeted with great enthusiasm, but only for a little while, because soon the cave filled up with smoke and everybody began to cough, and *that* scientist was thrown out into the cold.

Since then we have developed central heating, electric stoves, gas stoves, and all the comforts that we need indoors. We have come full cycle because now there is this great return to cooking outdoors, something which I refuse to do under all circumstances. With all of these indoor conveniences, one of my neighbors just last summer was cooking outdoors with an umbrella in the rain.

George Wald, a biologist at Harvard, has written that man has left the safeguards of instinctual life; we are on our own. Nature no longer takes care of us as once it did. That is the measure of our freedom: to chose our own way for good or evil. The Centennial speakers have emphasized the power of man's reasoning and the potential that can come from it. And they have stressed again and again the message that we do all belong to one family and that we are all traveling on just one spacecraft— this earth, this planet. I wish that what they said here could be carried to millions of readers and listeners. For I think it would all go very far in overcoming the tyranny of prejudice and the refusal to face reality, which are probably two of the roadblocks standing in front of the bright prospects for humanity.

CLARKE: I imagine Mr. Fuller would not agree with the modern geometers who say that if you can visualize it, it isn't geometry. I am horrified by his idea that our future foster parent will be the TV set. I was also amused, Mr. Fuller, by your brief prehistory of the AMA which does bear out some suspicions I have had for some time. Your remark that many of our domestic developments came from battleships and radio and some fallout from war was rather eloquently put by Bernard Shaw in the second part of *Man and Superman*, in a magnificent speech from the Devil to Don Juan, which castigates man and all his technical developments. It says how clumsy everything he does for peace is, because his heart is in his weapons. Well, this is the problem; it just seems to be true.

All through history man's heart has been in his weapons. Anything else has been done in his spare time, on the side. Finally, you said that you have known for the last twelve years that Malthus was wrong. That is rather a sweeping statement, isn't it? It is more apt to say that he was just slightly premature.

FULLER: If you want to call this a sweeping statement, then calling it a sweeping statement. Regarding those mathematicians working in the geometrics, they don't impress me at all. As far as I am concerned, all of their axioms are wrong. An axiom by definition defies the concepts of experimental science. These mathematicians insist that what is self-evident is not subject to further experimental demonstration; and therefore, as far as I am concerned, they are working with concepts which have no experimental foundation. I believe that about 90 per cent of all mathematics relates to games that have no valid relationship to real physical experience.

SHAPLEY: I agree with you that this is a great time to be alive and asking questions. That is what you implied. You also implied that we could be a success, "we" being mankind. But would we be? I like to remember that we are doing pretty well with what little equipment we have for comprehending what the world is and does. We do not have a hearing sense that can get us beyond our atmosphere. We have no cosmic sense of touch. We have one sense organ only by which we, including the astronomers, can try to find out about the outer world and that sense is sight. I wonder if there is a possibility that we will do something to enlarge our power of vision. We should realize that until recently, until Aristotle and his colleagues, we dealt with only one little segment of the electromagnetic spectrum. We could handle only one octave, you might say. And now, thanks to you and other ingenious people, our gadgetry has developed until we have more than fifty octaves that we can play with, that we can work with, that we can understand with. So again I would like to say that we *could* be a success, but will we be?

FULLER: Sir, I was talking about the prospects. I can look at the negative and the positive prospects, and I can say,

as Dr. Abelson's inventory showed me yesterday, that we are
on the way to using things up very rapidly. I can easily imagine
some Oswald getting his finger on one of the buttons that starts
the great retaliatory system going, and it would all be over for
mankind. And the more time we take to make man successful
the more chances there are of creating discontented and
antisocial Oswalds who can get fingers on those buttons. The
amount of time we have to review things here is too inadequate
for me to give you a very large amount of data about trends that
tend to make me feel that the prospects are positive. If I make
the prophecy that we are not going to come out all right, nobody
will be here to say that I was right or wrong. Therefore, I am
in a dangerous position. If I make a prophecy that I will come
out all right, then you are going to be around to see that I am
right. At any rate, the preponderance of the information is
that man will come out all right.

If it were up to man, I would assume that he would never
be a success. Realization of mutual success by all mankind is
frustrated by the now entirely irrelevant and invalid "inferiority"
or "failure" complex of world-around behaviors of humans,
conditioned exclusively by two million years of experience with
major failures of mankind, as well as with vital inadequacies of
vital necessities. Added to this is the ages-long, seemingly
obvious, and seemingly inevitable fact that the vast majority of
men would die at relatively early age through starvation, disease,
superstitiously governed human sacrifice, capital punishment,
war, or dueling as physical evolution whittled down the numbers
surviving to match the numbers supportable by the ignorantly
and only opportunistically exploited world resources.

Humanity's long-conditioned, reflexively supersitious
assumption is that man is designed to be a failure. The "normal"
human has always been a potential and probable failure. At an
early age, the average human acquires a powerful inferiority
complex from his exposure to his parents and his childhood
community's deeply inhibited culture of misinformation and
misfortune. The deep-seated proclivity of humans to gamble
their monies is founded on the working assumption of human
consciousness that individuals are inherently programmed for
failure and that only cultivated luck can divert the individual
from his negative plight. For only the last decade of all

history has total physical and economic success for all humanity been conceded by science to be feasible. Realization of this extraordinary potential is further frustrated by (1) rigid geographical and political partitioning of humanity under divisive and competitive ideological concepts, and (2) by the fact that scientific evolution, by which the success of humanity could be accomplished, is almost entirely invisible and its integrated significances are too difficult for total and effective comprehension by society.

I think man is still very innocent and helpless. But in chapter three of man's history that is now coming up, I see man actually beginning to transform from being utterly helpless and only subconsciously coordinate with important evolutionary events. We have gotten ourselves into a lot of trouble, but at the critical transformation stage, we are getting to a point where we are beginning to have some measurements and to know a little something. We are probably coming to the first period of direct, consciously-assumed responsibility of man in universe.

Until this period, all life has been able to succeed owing to nature's great anticipatory design of a regenerative ecological energy exchange. The mammals give off gases which are essential to the survival of the vegetation, while vegetation produces gases necessary to the continuation of animal life. None of them is conscious of contributing gratuitously to the vital support of the others. The earthworm is quite as irresponsibly, yet essentially, involved as the bee. All of life is inadvertently and unconsciously involved. All of life has designed subconscious drives which make it interconnectedly successful while being almost completely unwitting of the total ecological balance. The little bumblebee goes after his honey and his little fuzzy tail inadvertently knocks off and dusts pollen which fertilizes vegetation. I think that that is exactly the kind of pattern with which approximately all of humanity is preoccupied. I don't know any man who can stand up and say to us, "I am a success by virtue of having consciously designed, fabricated, and operated myself, the biosphere, the sun, the earth, and all the rest of intercomplemented ecology. I can tell you what I am doing with the lunch that I have just eaten: I am sending x amounts of this consumed energy to such and such gland to accomplish such and such work."

Humanity can't say that. Humanity as designed is over 90 per cent automated. Most humans can't even tell you why they have hair. They certainly can't tell you that they are consciously pushing each hair out through their heads in special shapes and colors for specific purposes. We don't know anyone who knows much about what he is doing and why. Humanity knows how to accidentally push buttons and make babies, but humanity doesn't really know yet how to make a baby. There are many indications, however, that man is just about to begin to participate consciously and somewhat more knowingly and responsibly in his own evolutionary transformation. I include evolution of the environment as a major part of the evolution of humanity. In his unconscious participation of the past, man has carelessly ruptured his earth, polluted his air and water, corrupted his children in order to sell any kind of toy guns, dope, smut, and product that would make sacrosanct money. Man has gotten himself into trouble with it. As Dr. Abelson's inventory showed us yesterday, man will have to become responsible or he won't be able to stay.

SHAPLEY: I think you are an optimist after all.

BOWMAN: The one thing I would say in respect to engineers and architects is that Bucky Fuller has been a third parent to both these professions for a long time. He probably feels that he has made no progress in convincing them of their wrong paths, but that is quite erroneous. The stimulation that Mr. Fuller has given every conservative, backward architect and engineer is very, very great. We need men like him in these professions and probably in others—people who go against the conservative attitude. I would hope that among these young people in the room there would be a good many who would like to emulate some of his thinking, his broad understanding of the world and his place in it. However, I would point out that they would have to be willing to be discouraged, and they would have to have a great deal of insight into the behavioral sciences as well as being engineers and architects. I hope Mr. Fuller goes on and on.

MENNINGER: Dr. Wescoe, you must be thinking what
a wonderful gift it is to be able to put ideas into new vivid forms
that enable all of us to begin thinking a little better. The
experience of this, of mind stretching, of mind shifting, is
wonderful. It is a splendid example of what a teacher must do,
what all of us wish we could do, as freely and as courageously
as the wonderful personality who has just been talking, giving
to us part of the enormous flow of materials going through his
his own mind so we can get little pieces of it to take home
with us, perhaps to cultivate and love.

ABELSON: As usual Buckminster Fuller has delivered an
interesting, wide-ranging talk. One aspect that I enjoyed, now
that we are approaching income tax time, was Mr. Fuller's
admonition to throw the rascals out, dispense with them.
I would like to be able to agree with him completely. However,
there were some little gaps in his description of how the young
were going to dispense with these rascals in Washington.
Also missing were some of the steps between the evil present
and the glorious future.

FULLER: My answer is that you will have to make them
obsolete. I don't try to reform Washington.

MAN AND THE FUTURE | 5

MAN
AND THE WORLD COMMUNITY
IN THE CENTURY AHEAD

Arthur Larson

As my beginning point and my pervasive theme I would like to make this observation: predictions of future worlds have typically been overfulfilled in the realm of the physical sciences and grotesquely underfulfilled in the realm of political, economic, and social organization. Indeed, some of our current science fiction writers have learned this lesson after having seen the supposedly fantastic worlds of H. G. Wells and Jules Verne made to look quaintly old-fashioned by the far more fantastic actuality of modern scientific achievements. And some of them now take pains to overshoot the mark of any conceivable scientific achievement by a comfortable margin, so that this can't happen to them. I suspect that by the time the incredibly difficult feat of placing man on the moon is achieved a considerable part of a generation nurtured on stories and cartoons of not merely interplanetary but interstellar travel will yawn and say, "What took you so long?" But in the realm of relations between man and man, between nation and nation, we have not only not begun to approach Utopia, we sometimes seem to be approaching the kind of anti-Utopia depicted in Orwell's 1984.

How shall we explain this, the achievements of science outstripping the most extravagant prophecies, while the relations between men and nations far from approaching any Utopian ideal seem always on the verge of reverting to the jungle?

One way of putting the answer is this: in the physical sciences man has learned to control and mold and direct the forces and materials supplied by nature for better or for worse. In human affairs he has not. Even as strong and wise a leader as Lincoln said, "I confess plainly that I have not controlled events, events have controlled me."

But to put the answer in this fashion is only to provoke the next question: why can not man learn to control himself in social, political, economic, and international affairs? The answer to this question in turn is that man has seldom applied to the conduct of human affairs even the most rudimentary techniques that he has for generations learned to use in discovering facts and putting them to work in the physical sciences.

If I may indulge in an extreme oversimplification, I would say there are three ways to approach knowledge: scientific, nonscientific, and pseudoscientific. The scientific approach begins with finding the true facts, through direct examination and experiment, and applying them and applying to them tested methods of analysis and verification. The nonscientific approach merely reacts blindly to the environment guided by nothing but instincts, emotions, prejudices, and superstitions. The pseudoscientific approach borrows the trappings of the scientific, including elaborate paraphernalia, complex demonstrations, and polysyllabic terminology. This approach, unfortunately, suffers from its failure to get the facts in the first place and its failure to test the facts and the results against reality.

The tragedy of man's attempt to bring order into his international, political, and social relations is that this attempt has floundered from the nonscientific to the pseudoscientific without ever coming to rest on the scientific. Before the age of science, if you wanted to find out what the inside of a human body was like, you didn't open a human body; you opened Aristotle. When Galileo, to test whether the speed of falling objects increased with their weight, dropped two balls of different weight from the leaning tower instead of looking it up in books, this was considered a piece of impertinence. Today we can hardly believe this story. Yet for the most part our conduct of political and international affairs is still dominated by pre-Galileo methods. Even the most far-reaching decisions of this century—the starting of wars, I was almost going to say—have been reached with less investigation of the facts than that a conscientious scientist would apply to the dietary habits of an obscure insect.

We know now that the Kaiser was convinced that the British would never enter World War I and that in his wildest dreams he never imagined that American would be aligned against him. With this lesson of history behind him, Hitler made precisely the same error. In fact, in neither instance is there any evidence that either of them made the slightest effort to check the true facts on which these momentous decisions rested. If you read the memoirs of Walter Hines Page, for example, you see the maddening frustration he went through when he tried to get somebody to listen to what he had to say as the ambassador to the Court of St. James on what the United States would probably do in World War I. And similarly we learned later that Hitler formed his judgment on probable British reaction on the strength of such data as the Oxford Union

Society's vote, after a debate in 1933, that "This House will not Fight for King and Country." If he had checked the facts about that debate he would have known—I happened to be there—that the vote was nothing but a tribute to the witty and the almost hypnotic eloquence of the philosopher C. E. M. Joad.

This is by no means confined to ourselves, or the Germans, or anybody else. The Communists probably have made the most grandiose application in history of the pseudoscientific approach to human affairs. Their jargon is shot through the appeals to scientific method, but their starting point is always a priori dogma rather than an investigation of facts. Basically their gaze is still riveted on a set of facts dated 1850. They are fighting the kind of raw capitalism that may or may not have existed a century ago but certainly does not exist now. Their ideology presupposes a species of human creature with motivations that direct observation quickly shows doesn't exist except in rare cases. For example, the urge to build the glorious Soviet society is supposed to displace completely such remnants of human cussedness as the acquisitive instinct. In practice, of course, we know that the Soviet Union, without admitting it, is now beginning to carry the incentive system to lengths not even seen in any private-enterprise economy.

By contrast, in the United States we seem at times to have exemplified the nonscientific approach with a kind of assumption that if everybody will just do what comes naturally the good life for all will somehow emerge. This view is typified by the economics of Adam Smith, and indeed the lusty surge of industrial and commercial progress in the western world owes much to the drives engendered by this attitude. But one of the products of this experience is this fragment of phony American folklore: that our society came into being as unselfconsciously as the unfolding of the petals of a flower, and that, although in personal and business life planning is the key to success, in public life planning is unqualifiedly evil. Even now many politicians think that the most devastating insult that you can hurl at an opponent is to call him a planner. This attitude goes back to the thirties when planning came to be associated with socialism and communism, and lesser ideas such as technocracy came under the same cloud. Perhaps as a result of the concern to show how different we were from the planned-from-above dictatorships, some of our best thinkers went to the opposite extreme and said that in our kind of society, planning and goals were useless. Walter Lippmann, for example, in *The Good Society*, says this over and over again: the good society has no architectural design, there are no blueprints, there is no plan of the future.

The true fact is that at certain key points in American history Americans have applied the true scientific approach by first studying the facts, then conceiving a definite design and building toward order. An outstanding example is our constitution. The British constitution just grew. But the American Constitution was the product of a gigantic effort of intellectual research and creativity. When the great farmlands of this part of the country opened up in the Midwest, Americans concluded that the west was going to be a country of small family farms. The result was the Homestead Act, a conception of breathtaking scope and imagination which methodically translated this blueprint into reality. In South Dakota, where my grandfather homesteaded, since they were short of trees they added that to get your homestead you had to plant a certain number of trees. As a result, to this day, when you fly over South

Dakota, on every 160 acres you will see a wood lot which forms a windbreak and also a source of timber.

On the industrial side, although the persistence of laissez-faire thought permitted the growth of the cartel system in Europe, Americans looked at the facts of their life rather than the pages of Adam Smith and saw what was the end result of "perfect competition." They deliberately decided that the American economy was going to be non-monopolistic and, with this design before them, went straight to the point and passed the Sherman Antitrust Act, the Clayton Act, and the Norris-LaGuardia Act. Again Americans by direct observation of the facts before them saw that the bargaining power of organized labor was not equal to that of employers and set out to make it at least approximately so, by devising and subsequently revising the Wagner Labor Relations Act. On the international scene after World War II the facts showed that everyone's peace and welfare depended upon the economic and technical rebuilding and development of the devastated cities of Europe and then of the newly developing countries of Africa and Asia, and the magnificent concept of economic and technical aid was the deliberately designed result.

I suppose the area outside of the physical sciences where the authentic scientific approach has been most successfully applied is that of economics, particularly in the prevention of severe recessions and the reconciling of free enterprise with orderly growth. One reason is that economists now have an impressive array of reliable current facts on which to act, in the form of economic indicators, touching investment, saving and spending, income, sales, inventories, employment, prices, and dozens of other categories of facts and data. Careful study of past experience now enables economists to watch these dials, notice the need for some adjustment, turn a knob here, tighten a valve there, on discount rates, taxes, government purchase policies, social insurance, fiscal measures, and the trouble is righted. Above all, this is possible because we have accepted now that this scientific handling of the problem is normal. We have rejected the anachronistic judgment of the nonscientific who think that business should merely be left alone and the pseudoscientific who want to invoke Adam Smith and Ricardo rather than get out in the hot sun and look at the facts of contemporary life.

But of all the areas in which the need to control events rather than be controlled by them is urgent that of international relations plainly is of the highest priority. If the human mind fails here, all the success of the human mind in other fields will be dragged down into failure by the ultimate insanity of nuclear war. How are we doing in applying the power of intelligence in this most crucial of all human tasks? The answer is that, until recently at any rate, it has never occurred to the world's leaders that the techniques of intelligence and intellectual research had anything to contribute to solving the problem of war or of building the world community.

A rational approach to any problem begins with getting the facts, facts which are accurate and current. International relations today, if they are based on facts at all, are generally based on facts from eighteen to three hundred years out of date. More often than not, they are not based on facts at all but on fictions. Is it any wonder that the results don't make any sense? Arthur C. Clarke tells us that the handling of science fiction must be based on facts. The handling of facts in international affairs is being based on fictions.

I should like now to submit a kind of checklist of fictions

bearing on the ultimate issue of war and peace and on the measures which must be taken to dispose of international disputes in order to build a world community in the century ahead. The first fiction is that diplomacy is the only valid method of settling international disputes. The true fact is, as direct observation will clearly confirm, that old-fashioned power-politics diplomacy—almost the only technique used in international relations—is obsolete. We can understand, then, why all of the world's cold war problems—divided Germany, divided Korea, divided China, divided Vietnam, to name only the most obvious illustrations—are as far from solution as they were when they first arose.

Why is diplomacy obsolete? The reason is that war, as we have all been told a thousand times, is unusable as an instrument of national policy. By war I mean a large scale all-out war as we have come to know it in this century. It is unusable legally because we have made it so in the United Nations Charter. It is unusable practically because the possible extinction of all life—at any rate in the Northern Hemisphere—which might result from all-out nuclear war, is, if I may use the language of the Pentagon, unacceptable. Practically everybody in the world can understand and accept this, with the possible—at least verbal—exception of the Communist Chinese. But what is not understood is that when war becomes obsolete methods of dispute-settling that depended upon the ultimate availability of war themselves become obsolete. Old-fashioned diplomacy was not typically an exercise in finding the intrinsic rights and wrongs of the controversy, such as a boundary dispute. The outcome didn't depend on evidence produced by the old plats, the old maps. No, what the parties to a diplomatic confrontation were concerned about was which one could defeat the other if matters came to a military showdown.

If country A convinced country B that in such a showdown A would win, through diplomacy the boundary would move to the disadvantage of B. But if they couldn't convince each other, the dispute would go on and on. Pressures would mount. Tensions would mount. Ultimately there would be a blowup. There would be a war. At any rate the air would be cleared. The boundary would move to the disadvantage of the loser, the pieces would be picked up, and the story would start over again. That's history more or less, somewhat oversimplified.

All this now has been changed. Something new has been added to this process which completely disrupts it. Because of the unusability of nuclear weapons we have complete military deadlock between the great powers on the major issues. A fact of life is that when you have military deadlock you have diplomatic deadlock. And yet in the teeth of this plainly observable fact, we go on trying to settle disputes by diplomacy as if we were in the days of Machiavelli or Metternich.

The second fiction closely related to the first is that in all international situations it is military power that ultimately counts. We have just seen that between the nuclear giants the only effect of their immense power is not to gain advantage but to preserve a stalemate. But even as between a nuclear power and a small power, nuclear power is virtually useless, as we are learning in Vietnam. There is no evidence that the Soviet Union in its quarrel with Communist China enjoys any advantage because of its overwhelming superiority in military strength. Poland and the other Warsaw Pact countries are taking a more independent line toward Moscow than before Russia acquired nuclear armaments. The overwhelming destructive capacity of the United States is of no use in relations to Cuba; it does not prevent such humiliating episodes as the Bay of Pigs invasion nor is it of any relevance in the Dominican Republic, Malaysia, Yemen, Cyprus, the northern Indian border, or in many trouble spots of Africa and Asia and around the world. In the Congo poisoned darts figured prominently but not nuclear weapons.

The third fiction is that nations cannot bring themselves to settle their disputes, their important disputes, by peaceful means such as arbitration and adjudication. The true fact is that nations have repeatedly submitted controversies involving high interests and high public excitement to peaceful settlement. During the nineteenth century 177 major disputes between nations were resolved by arbitration including 79 in which the United States was a party. Nor will it do to try to explain this away by saying that nations really submit only unimportant disputes for arbitration. No controversy in international affairs is more emotion-packed, regardless of its size, than a dispute over territory. One recalls Hamlet's soliloquy about how a nation will fight over a strip of ground not big enough to bury the dead in. And yet Norway gave up East Greenland to Denmark, a territory bigger than both of them put together I am sure, as a result of an international court decision. And who was it that Hamlet was talking about in his soliloquy? Norway. So we can do better. In the last few years boundary disputes important enough to provoke armed conflict between Nicaragua and Honduras, between Cambodia and Thailand, have been settled in the World Court.

As a matter of fact adjudication and arbitration on the merits is usually the only way in which a hotly disputed contest can be settled. The reason is that no government can make a diplomatic settlement giving away the sacred soil of the motherland even in a small amount and survive politically at home. But a judicial decision reaching the same result can be handed down, as it was in these cases, without fatal impact on the political fortunes of the incumbent government at home.

The fourth fiction is that since there is no world government with overwhelming military power to enforce law nations won't pay any attention to judicial or arbitral decisions that they don't like. The actual fact is that there is no case on record of disobedience to the decisions of the present international court's predecessor; and only one fraction of one decision of the present international court has been disobeyed. Among the hundreds and thousands of other arbitral, judicial, mixed claims commissions, and other awards, which are the subject of a large research study at my own research center, we have not been able to find more than twenty out of thousands where the question of compliance has ever been raised. We have been in touch with the foreign office of every country that has ever been involved in an international dispute. It is well known among international lawyers that international decisions are, if anything, better complied with than the decisions of domestic tribunals.

Running through all our international misconceptions is an entire network of outdated ideas about the Soviet Union, communism, and the cold war. One such idea is that the Soviet Union never changes. The fact is that when the events in that area since the death of Stalin are seen in historical perspective it may very well be said that a greater change has taken place in the Soviet Union than has ever been achieved in any major country without revolution in a similar period of time.

A like fallacy is an assertion that all totalitarian regimes are alike and that there really is no difference between

Khrushchev's Russia and Hitler's Germany. Let me cite just one of the many interesting differences that could be adduced—one that has perhaps not had the attention that it deserves. The entire force of Hitler's immense propaganda machine was devoted to preparing the German people to accept war, whereas everywhere you travel in the Soviet Union today you encounter nothing but propaganda for peace. This is not a facade for outsiders. I have been to Russia three times in the last few years and traveled quite a bit off the beaten path. In little villages you see banners across the street that might be announcing socials, basketball games, or something. But usually these banners across the street say "peace and friendship."

I am not unaware of the problem of reconciling Russian words and Russian policies in this area of seeking peace. I merely want to point out here that if the Soviet Union at some future time elected to plunge into the flagrantly warlike, aggressive course that Hitler took it would have to reckon with an entire generation, that instead of having been trained to regard war as noble and inevitable, as was the case with the Hitler youth, has been infused day and night with the message that war is the greatest of all evils, and peace is the highest objective.

In the same bundle of outdated notions is the idea that all conflicts in the world can be ultimately explained as communism versus anti-communism. It would be difficult to calculate how many blunders of policy and errors of strategy this persistent fallacy has produced and is still producing. A large part of the quarrels that are going on around the world today goes back to animosities and rivalries that were old long before there was anything such as communism—between Arabs and Jews, between Hindus and Moslems, between dozens of African tribes, between Greeks and Turks, between innumerable nations and groups and religions and factions in all parts of the world with old scores to settle and new frictions attendant upon the decoloniali-zation process. True, communism is not averse to fishing in these troubled waters; but that is quite a different matter from supposing that if communism could somehow be made to go away the world's conflicts would largely disappear.

The bi-polar picture of world conflict is discredited even more decidedly by the very real break between the Soviet Union and Communist China. It has become crystalline clear that this is no mere ideological difference. It is a dead-earnest, national struggle between two natural rivals involving by far the largest territorial dispute in the world, a life and death battle for the allegiance of the world's population, and a growing racial conflict that could dwarf any racial conflict we have yet seen as Communist China tries to mobilize racialism on a global basis.

At this point in my list I'm tempted to say that almost every major foreign policy we have is based on fiction rather than fact. Take the German problem. Some people still think it is the most important problem in the world. What is the core of our German policy? It is the utterly unrealistic fiction that Germany will be reunited under free all-German elections. The China problem is certainly in the same high category. What is our policy here? The fiction that Chiang's regime is the government of all China even now. Chiang himself, by the way, pays a very high cash price for this fiction. Did you know that when the dues for the United Nations are assessed they are based upon population and upon gross national product? Chiang is paying dues to the U.N. based on the totality of the population of Taiwan and mainland of China. We compound this fiction by the assumption that the People's Republic of China, approaching a fourth of the world's population, does not exist—for diplomatic purposes.

In Vietnam, just to take a sampling, we persist in the fiction that the Viet Cong does not exist, diplomatically or politically, as a belligerent with which we must negotiate if we want an end to the shooting. According to Senator Mansfield, and I have not seen it questioned, between 8 per cent and 10 per cent of the people we are shooting at and being shot by are from North Vietnam. The other 90 odd per cent are South Vietnamese Viet Cong. They are real enough on the end of the rifle. They are nonexistent for diplomatic purposs. Secretary Rusk the other day so far forgot himself as to deliver what must be one of the most illogical statements in this incredibly chaotic story of Vietnam. He said, "Why should we negotiate with these fellows merely because they have rifles in their hands?" What are we negotiating about? We want the shooting to stop. Who does the shooting? People with rifles in their hands. Therefore, we should negotiate with people with rifles in their hands.

It is these situations on which our security, our survival, perhaps the survival of humanity depends. And they are being handled on inaccurate or outdated facts at best or at worst on outright fictions. And we are paying the price. You can no more flout real facts on the international scene than you can in space travel if you want to get a successful result. Would a moon landing be successful if instead of carefully making studies of the texture and the composition of the moon surface the space planners posited that the moon is made of green cheese? And yet the astronauts will sooner find that the moon is made of green cheese than you and I will see a reunited China governed by Chiang Kai-shek.

This then is a mere sampling or erroneous notions

which too often take the place of fact. The list could be extended to other items large or small. What is to be done about this dangerous state of affairs? The fundamental requisite is the acceptance of the idea that the techniques of research, scholarship, and the scientific method have much more to contribute to the amelioration of national troubles than has ever been suspected.

It is curious how difficult it is to get this idea accepted. I recall that at one of our Soviet-American citizens' conferences that have been going on for the past five years, bringing together top leaders in all walks of life in both countries, we were trying to demonstrate that a three-man troika to run the United Nations Secretariat in place of a single Secretary-General wouldn't work. One of my colleagues, Prof. Louis Sohn from the Harvard Law School, cited a detailed research study at Harvard of how committees, boards, and small human groups worked in different sizes and combinations in governmental, corporate, and nonprofit organizations and every conceivable kind of human collective activity. The study clearly showed that of all possible bodies the three-man committee is the worst. All of you committee members know what I mean. One reason is the tendency, familiar to anybody who has served on a three-man committee group, of two to gang up on the third. Every triumvirate has its Lepidus and its Caesar. I gently reminded the Russians that they recently had a demonstration of this phenomenon in the triumvirate that succeeded Stalin. On the other hand the study showed that a board of five or seven or nine would generally eliminate most of these difficulties. I pointed out to the Russians that if a comparable study with a comparable mass of data had shown what happens when you combine two hydrogen atoms with one oxygen atom they wouldn't hesitate to to accept the validity of the result. But because it had to do with human affairs apparently we have to ignore the observed facts and go on making the same mistakes forever.

Plainly, if human affairs are going to be ordered by the scientific method rather than by fictions, it is the university that must take the lead. And in so doing it must exploit to the full both of its traditional functions: first, that of being the intellectual center of the community, and, second, that of being the teacher of future leaders. Everybody in the university community is aware that there has been a running debate for a long time on whether the university's sole function is to teach students or whether it has a function of producing knowledge through research. With a sharp increase in sponsored research, on most campuses a large part of it in the natural sciences, and a large part financed by the government, some professors seem to take the attitude that this is a recent and somewhat illegitimate invasion of resources and of personnel in the university. To come down to the mundane symptoms of this attitude, you will find on many campuses right now that the members of the research staffs, although they may have more advanced degrees and higher academic qualifications than some of the members of the teaching staff, are still treated as second-class citizens when it comes to things like fringe benefits, such as housing and tenure.

Perhaps the quickest way to set this matter straight, since these critics frequently like to think of themselves as appealing to tradition of the university, is to remind them that historically the university was not first a teaching institution. To take a classical example, Oxford's earliest beginning dates from a time when a group of monks settled in the swampy area where the Thames and the Cherwell come together—some sort of self-abnegation makes people put universities in the worst possible climate—and there they devoted themselves to keeping medieval learning alive, copying and illuminating manuscripts, and writing glosses upon the works of ancient sages—in short, what passed in medieval times for research. Inevitably students appeared and begged to sit at the feet of the learned masters. At first rebuffed, they persisted; then finally the monks grudgingly gave in and let them stay if they wouldn't interfere too much with the other more important tasks. That's how the universities started. And to this day we have one college at Oxford which is a reminder of this origin, All Souls, the college that has no students.

You can imagine how pleased I was when in the material handed me when I arrived I found a handsome booklet entitled *What Is a University?* And on the very first page, I read: "The university concept was born in medieval monastaries. To their museum collections of treasured manuscripts came scholars. Students followed, and the scholars became teachers as well. These four elements have defined the university ever since: the museum, the scholar, the teacher, and the student. Lacking any of them an institution is something less than a university." I say any university that announces this credo is well equipped to head into the next century. This also means that research and production of knowledge, as such, particularly in international affairs, now must be recognized not merely as essential but even as respectable, in academic circles, in university administration circles, and not least in the great, private grant-making foundations.

About seven or eight years ago there was a turning in this story, the upsurge of what might be called the peace research movement. The central conviction of this movement is that scholars and research workers have an important part to play in the building of the structures that are essential to a world community in the century ahead, and in the prevention of war in the meantime. I suppose that the physical sciences must be credited with having taken the lead in this instance, too. At a time, for example, when inspection was the cornerstone of our disarmament policy, it soon became evident that if we were to become serious about disarmament we would have to know a great deal more scientifically than we knew at the time about how to detect underground explosions. For example, how many little black boxes would you have at what distance to detect what kind of explosions? Otherwise how could we talk about inspection? And so a sharp increase in the amount of scientific investigation was launched in order to make some sense about inspection when negotiated internationally and politically.

Some of the rest of us began to realize that we had to know some other things for this same negotiation. If we are going to promise inspection, we have to know some things about law. Suppose we promised inspection and suppose we actually got a disarmament agreement; and one day the disarmament inspector, a Russian, turned up at Union Carbide, knocked on the door and said, "We are the Russians. We are the inspectors. Open the doors. We want to come in and look the whole place over." The manager stands at the door and says, "Private property. Keep out." Now where are we? Have we got a legal right as a federal government to promise the Russians that they can inspect our private plants? We ought to know before we make that the cornerstone of our policy. One of the earliest books produced in what I regard as the peace research movement was a book on this whole legal problem, inspection in connection with disarmament.

The economists have much to contribute, because we have to know, if we really disarm, what happens to our economy. Under the surface, perhaps without admitting it maybe, a lot of people in this country are worried about the fact that if we could achieve disarmament we would have a depression. A lot of people would be thrown out of work. Well, we had better know. So elaborate studies were launched, and they are still going on, not only about a broad sweep of the question of the economic effect of disarmament but the impact on particular plants and particular products.

Along this line research centers began to be formed for the express purpose of methodically doing this job, in all the different disciplines. Our Rule of Law Research Center at Duke was founded in 1958 and now has a staff of twenty-seven. Early in the game I made for the Rule of Law Center a list of thirteen research jobs that at the time seemed to need doing. Parkinson's Law has set in and the list is over a hundred now. But we and other centers and individuals and law schools and professional associations are methodically working away on this list. The same kind of lists were made up under the auspices of a little group formed called Peace Research Committee and later the Peace Research Institute, Inc., a corporation. We have similar lists in economics and physical sciences, psychology and decision making, and in communications. The importance of this whole effort is now reflected in the prominent place occupied by research in the purposes and budgets of the Arms Control and Disarmament Agency.

The significance of this is that for the first time we are witnessing a massive and methodical intellectual assault upon the stubborn problems, both fundamental and detailed, whose solution is a precondition to any world community in the century ahead. This is not a matter of preaching peace in generalities or slogans, nor is it a matter of dreaming up shining models of totally reconstructed world orders. It's a matter of beginning with what we have, within the limits of the possible, and finding ways both to handle today's troubles more effectively and to construct gradually better laws, procedures, and institutional arrangements, for the settling of all disputes and the prevention of all threats to the peace as they arise. The world we hope to build in this way may not be much more Utopian a hundred years from now than our present world. But it should not be much worse either. And that, in view of the cumulating crescendo of threats and dangers, would be in the long story of man's search for world community a triumph of sorts in itself.

COMMENTARIES

LARRABEE: When the Denver poet, Tom Ferril, was asked shortly after World War II what he anticipated for the coming hundred years, he said, "Peace among the great nations but a lot of fender-bumping." And certainly fender-bumping is what we have now, and what has become the face of war as our generation—the new generation—now knows it. Certainly it is true that war is among our least-studied subjects, one that we know very little about.

We know, for example, very little about how people cross over that mysterious boundary between a peace-loving state of mind and a warlike state of mind. If you had possessed all the techniques of social science and had studied the American people on December 6, 1941, you would have found them divided; you would have found them strongly isolationist; you would have great doubt as to what they would do if faced with a challenge. And if you had studied them on December 8 you would have found them strangely and incredibly united in what was then a really most risky, problematical, quixotic, military enterprise. And we know very little about what happened in the minds of millions upon millions of Americans during those two days.

As a critic of Dr. Larson's speech, I am somewhat in the position of having to disagree with a plea on behalf of rational analysis and peace, which means being in favor of irrationality and war, so I will do the best I can. I am a little surprised that he so wholeheartedly endorses the injection of scientific methods and rationality into military problems, since this particular effort today is associated with the name of a most unpopular man, Robert McNamara. You perhaps know the story of the admiral in the Pentagon who presented himself at Bethesda and asked to see a psychiatrist, and when he was finally admitted he said he was suffering from severe depression. And the psychiatrist said, "Let me speculate about you; don't tell me, let me guess. You were a carrier pilot in World War II?"

He said, "That's right."

"You had a tour of duty in Korea?"

"That's right."

"So it is perfectly clear you had a vigorous, active life and now you are condemned to being passive and fenced in by all this bureaucracy. What you ought to do is restore some excitement to your life. Why don't you go down and stand outside the Russian Embassy and wait until a high-ranking military man comes out and go up to him and say, 'To hell with Kosygin!' It will set your glands going."

A day or two later the psychiatrist looked out the window and an ambulance drew up and out came this battered form all bandaged up, on a stretcher. Sure enough, it was the admiral. When he went down and asked what happened, the admiral said, "I told this Russian military man, 'To hell with Kosygin!'—we were standing right in the middle of the street—and he said, 'To hell with Robert McNamara,' and we were shaking hands when this truck hit us."

The difficulty Mr. McNamara faces is that the problems of war are less rational than the problems of internal organizations in the Department of Defense. He and his very able analytically-minded assistants can solve problems of budgeting, can solve problems of cost accounting, different kinds of weapons systems, and the like. But they cannot analyze and cannot cost account what goes on in the mind of the Viet Cong guerilla fighting in the jungle, a man engaged in what must seem to us an irrational act. It is irrational for a helpless, virtually unarmed man to take on the Strategic Air Command, but it doesn't seem irrational to him. He can argue to himself that throwing a grenade into a restaurant full of American officers in Saigon is just as effective militarily as a multimillion dollar B-52 bomber—and in fact it very well may be. The difficulty of war is that it so involves men's will and their bravery, or whatever else you want to call it, that these careful calculations can become not only difficult to use but sometimes completely irrelevant.

I would argue that it isn't entirely true, as Dr. Larson was saying, that military deadlock and diplomatic deadlock necessarily go together, or that this is in fact the situation that we face. War, to the sorrow of all of us, still has a role to play in allowing men's will to confront one another, allowing strength to parley with strength, as it did in the terrible days of the Cuban missile crisis. The only motto I have to offer is Napoleon's: "If it were merely a matter of avoiding risk, glory would be at the disposition of very mediocre talent."

EISELEY: I am gratified that Dr. Larson has spoken so ably about the rationality of the scientific approach on certain of these matters, because if ever rationality was needed it is needed now. And I recognize also the problems which have been presented by Dr. Larrabee. I would like to go on and comment; in a sense it will be a quick résumé of the theme that I have already attempted to present.

It seems to me that there are two dangers we face in connection with science and our approach to these problems. One is the danger in the assumption, which in a sense exists in the public domain, that science is a cure-all. I think the public would be better prepared for the problems of our effort if it were to understand that science is not alone the solver of problems but a creator of problems. This is not an anti-scientific statement. This fact, however, is one that we have to recognize, because every time we produce a new invention and it passes over into the technological phase, we create or set in motion a vast series of social changes which follow along as consequences, and which may or may not be advantageous. At any rate they have to be surveyed, in turn, by the social sciences. I think that it is this, essentially, which Dr. Larson is trying to urge upon us with a full recognition of the fact that we are not in the doorway of Utopia. Nor are we apt to be, in the world which exists; nevertheless we can attempt to apply some rational thinking in this area. A rational approach is partly dependent upon public understanding that the scientist does not have anything magical at his command, that these problems are created frequently by science, and that they multiply at a sort of geometric rate, particularly as the rapidity of their introduction into society increases.

One doesn't even have to turn to the international scene in this connection. Ideas and inventions have a way of escaping their original inventors who may have had other purposes in mind and of creeping out—as I once phrased it—like noxious insects into the social fabric. Take, for example, the development of the electronic snooping devices that we have read so much about in the last few years and which threaten the privacy of everyone, and whose control is extremely difficult. Here is a situation not glimpsed, perhaps, originally but one which presents a very real problem, the sort of spying, for example, that goes on between one great corporate body and another. I am not even considering the international aspect of spying. This type of local situation has to be taken account of.

Occasionally scientific colleagues say, "This is all very well, but what's it got to do with me? I am a scientist. I discover, and what the public does and what politicians do with what I discover is none of my business." That is, I submit, an archaic attitude in science. It may have had a certain point years ago in terms of—let us say—some investigation into the basic aspects of the universe, but when the death of a world may depend upon the kind of discoveries an individual scientist might make, then I submit that the very denial of interest in values or in ethics implies something about the individual. The scientist who says he has no interest in values is revealing a dreadful sense of values on his own part.

I think it is a very healthy sign that in spite of the vast streams of money flowing around in the military industrial complex there are men, scientists of great distinction, who have been concerned with such problems and have spoken of them. They have attempted, among other things, to point out that even with all the multiplications of our institutions of learning the amount of our scientific talent is not such that we can endlessly fire away our wealth into outer space without some consideration of the consequences in terms of the application of huge funds and, more importantly, the application of distinguished and rare minds to the other problems of our society. The truth is the amount of this talent is not limitless; even as a very rich state our wealth is not limitless. The time is coming when choices as to what areas of science we may most justly devote ourselves to will have to be made. This partly depends, of course, on the international situation.

I might add that the anthropologist could say that societies sometimes have a way of becoming involuted, that their emphasis upon particular instiutions may grow distorted enough that after a while the whole thing is askew. As an example, it may involve the emphasis upon some religion which has seized control of the major wealth of the society, as has happened in several instances in the remote past, or on the other hand the development of an enormous, malignant, threatening cancer in the sense of such profound expenditure and concentration upon the weapons of war that a society more and more becomes fixed in a channel, as Dr. Larson pointed out. In any event it becomes so increasingly difficult to pull this society back into a position of normality, economically, without seriously upsetting it that no single individual can any longer achieve this.

I believe that President Eisenhower, before going out of office, warned of the danger of just such a growth of this complex, and it is something that is still with us. In this connection let me add that a variety of types of men become involved with science so that when the nature of science as a social institution changes there will always be those men, however able, however brilliant, who have to be watched in terms of concentration of power. The flow of wealth in these channels brings to the surface the scientific entrepreneur who in other times and other places has operated elsewhere. These are among the fundamental problems which science has to face.

Though the pursuit of knowledge demands objectivity, which is written into the scientific credo, it also demands a recognition of truth and a value system of its own.

MENNINGER: The discussion is far out of my competence, but I would like to ask some questions. I so much admire what Dr. Eiseley just said about the essentiality of a value system in science that I want to second that, if I may, before asking an impertinent question. I was much impressed by what Dr. Larson said, too, and by the information about research that is being carried on; but I'll frame my question. Science— the scientific method—assumes its certain data are collectable and organizable; are subject to drawing certain tentative conclusions. What puzzles me, as a very ignorant layman, is how can you be sure about the raw data upon which the scientific conclusions are formed? Sometime ago I read a book called *The Ugly American*, by Burdick and Lederer. Now they have written another book called *Sarkhan*, which I also read. I want to ask Dr. Larson if he is acquainted with the book?

LARSON: Not the second book.

MENNINGER: Now the second book is similarly fictional in form. It described Burdick's and Lederer's own experiences with the unreliability of the data furnished news correspondents and foreign representatives about situations far remote from us. I found it a very disturbing book. I think the authors were disturbed by what they feel to be their discoveries in this area. To think that the very information we read may be entirely fabricated or based upon entirely unreliable sources even though it comes through very good news media and may be completely believed by the persons who collected it—you have the same uncanny sensation you have when you read a mystery story like the *The Spy That Came in From the Cold*. The deception he receives is deceiving the other fellow about the deception; nobody knows quite who is deceiving whom, and which information is manufactured by whom for what purpose. For scientists accustomed to having their patients or their guinea pigs make some effort to present the facts of their existence to him for study, this sort of deception—this sort of unreliability is the basic data of the conditions in foreign countries—seems to me to put all of us at a disadvantage and to make us sympathetic with the great difficulties which must beset the research that Dr. Larson described.

I wondered if you wouldn't talk about that a little bit, if not to reassure us at least to warn us that it is true that some things we read are not the truth—if I may put it that way—and even the people who give us the information do not realize that what they are giving us is not so.

MONTAGU: I couldn't agree more with what Dr. Larson presented to us this evening and also with my colleague Loren Eiseley, and I point out that the god of the common man's idolatry in our own time is the scientist. Thereby hangs the kind of danger that Dr. Eiseley has so eloquently presented to you, because we do tend to believe that there is something magical about this creature who invented the atom bomb. Having invented the atom bomb and seen to what use it was put, one of the makers of the atom bomb eventually brought himself to see what he and his colleagues had done and declared that "we have known sin."

This is not good enough. It is desirable to recognize the consequences of one's conduct as a scientist before the damage is done. To stand by with handwashing indifference and say, "I am a scientist and I am engaged in discovering; what others do with my discoveries is no concern of mine," is the height of immorality. No person should purport ever to enter into any activity, particularly with reference to animate nature and especially man, without asking himself what the consequences of his conduct will be for animate nature and for man. I would say, with all respect to Dr. Larson, that science is not enough, that in this tribute we have been paying to scientists we have neglected to understand that first and foremost the scientist is a human being, that it is humanity which will always have to be the context in which he works. The approaches to the solution of human problems have to be primarily human approaches and not scientific ones. The scientific investigation of the nature of the problem is highly important, and here I couldn't agree more with Dr. Larson; but those scientific approaches must not be left to scientists to use. They must be left to human beings who have by their conduct evidenced their ability to see the problem as a human problem. I suspect that Dr. Larson would agree with this. It is not sufficient to leave war, as a great French politician said, to the generals. The problem of human and international conflict is far too important to leave to either generals or politicians. As Aldous Huxley pointed out years ago in one of his novels, if you look in any encyclopedia for a definition of intelligence you will always find it defined, in descending order of merit, as human intelligence, animal intelligence, and military intelligence. Hence, I deplore the delight which American universities take, when a presidency of an institution bcomes available, in seeking out some broken-down general or admiral for such an important position.

Here, I think, we see the evidence of one of the root causes of the disasters from which we are suffering, and that is the failure in critical ability of the people themselves who are responsible for such conduct. We are here engaged in listening to and discussing in a dialogue what we can do about the human situation at this present critical time, yet I wonder how many persons in this room who have agreed with what has been said are in support of what is going on now in Vietnam. If the majority of us in this room and in other rooms like this saw how wrong and how evil what we are doing in Vietnam is, there would not be this kind of approach to this kind of a solution of a problem—which is not a solution to the problem at all, but which can only end in disaster. I think it is extremely important that while we are attempting to find scientific solutions to these international problems we also engage in the problem of attempting to teach our students in our schools and in our universities how to use their minds critically and efficiently, so that when they are presented with the evidence by a graduate of the Harvard Business School and a Ford Company employee, who by these credentials is elected a minister of war, that they are able to evaluate what he says and do what they ought about it.

LARSON: I think the commentators have greatly clarified and given dimension and depth to what I was able to say in the time available. Dr. Menninger, with his well-known incisive-ness, has gone right to the heart of the difficulty which largely

accounts for the problem that I outlined, that is, the lingering
question whether you really can to any degree apply anything
of the scientific method to human affairs. Mr. Montagu has
helped me when he said that what we can really study is not
the mysteries of the human spirit or the innermost recesses
of inner motivation, but we can study certain objective facts
and most of all adopt an attitude of mind that believes this
kind of study is important and that will accept and act upon
facts as they are found and not put in their place emotions,
prejudices, political expediencies.

Dr. Menninger's question and particularly his reference to
the book by Mr. Burdick and Mr. Lederer actually underlines
my point, which is that too often today we are being given as
a people inaccurate and distorted facts, sometimes deliberately
and sometimes carelessly, and since we are a government of the
people this in turn may have a lot to do with the fact that we
are getting the wrong decisions made.

Let me take one specific illustration of how objective facts
could have been handled quite differently at the time of the
Dominican intervention. I think it is clear to anybody now
who will honestly make a study of the facts that the whole theory
and the whole factual basis of that unfortunate intervention
was false. The idea that this was a Communist uprising in
the Dominican Republic has now been denied by the
Communists themselves. The Communist party was very
small, in fact, there was less communism in the Dominican
Republic than any place in Latin America at that time. The
Communist party of the Dominican Republic later went to a
Communist meeting; there the Communist leaders, in the best
tradition, beat their breasts and confessed why they hadn't
taken the initiative in the Dominican intervention. They were
asking absolution and forgiveness from their brethren.

In that instance the trouble was simply, first of all, that
the right people were not consulted. The people who had biases
and prejudices were relaying information that was wildly
inaccurate for reasons I do not pretend to plumb: President
Johnson somehow was led to the point of saying that fifteen
hundred people had their heads cut off. There wasn't even one.
There was plenty of time for investigation in the meantime of
things like this, which are not mysteries of human spirits;

they are simply facts. Either there were Communists dominating the Dominican uprising or there were not. This can in fact be investigated, and there were plenty of people who knew the facts.

Mr. Montagu has brought up the subject which is on everyone's mind and which we can never entirely stay away from, the tragedy in Vietnam. I could greatly enlarge my list if I were to go down the list of all of the blunders of fact and the misconceptions that have led to that unfortunate affair. I don't think—and this is central to my main theme—that anybody at any one moment made a big wrong decision that we were going to have a quarter of a million men fighting in Vietnam. We slid into this thing. We nibbled our way into it. A hundred men here and a hundred men there and thousand men here and ten thousand men there. The first thing you know it is a quarter of a million, and nobody knows what it will be a year from now. And from the very start it was one mistaken fact, one misconception, after another.

Let me take my own field of law for example. The state of law is a fact which can be investigated from the very start of this military action in Vietnam. We were told by the administration that we had to do this because we had a commitment made by President Eisenhower in 1954 in a letter to President Diem. I happened to know that story because I was attending cabinet meetings at the time. I followed the closing days and months of the Indo-China war, and I took the rather outrageous step of going and getting the letter itself, which apparently nobody else had done. It was being cited in every speech as the reason why we had to fight in Vietnam, because we had been committed, morally committed, and it would be morally outrageous, it would be unthinkable not to fight—the same reason over and over again, always starting with that letter in October, 1954. I read the letter. It had six sentences in it. It was an extremely tentative, highly conditional offer to begin negotiations about the possibility of technical aid in South Vietnam, provided there were governmental reforms, provided the government got the confidence of the people, provided there was a unified and reformed society, and so on. All tentative and conditional. Nothing in there about fighting their battles or anything of the sort. Now this is a fact—the contents of the letter. We don't hear it cited anymore. The mistake has been exposed in the meantime, but in its place we are being told we are committed by the SEATO treaty. Well I got out the SEATO treaty when this was first said. In a little book some of you have seen, I carefully analyzed with standard legal techniques the commitment of the SEATO treaty, and I found without the slightest doubt that there wasn't any legal commitment in the SEATO treaty for us to fight in South Vietnam. I've taken the precaution of checking that conclusion with two successive legal advisers to the State Department, and they both agreed with me. And yet we are told as recently as a few weeks ago by the Secretary of State, the President, and others that we are committed by the SEATO treaty to fight in South Vietnam. Now here is a question that can be settled, settled by normal methods of investigation, starting with getting the treaty out and reading it—which is a pretty good way to start. It is much further than many people generally go. This may confirm my main theme again, that when you retrace those steps and sometimes when you see them happening at close range, you begin to realize that these earth-shaking decisions on which the welfare of the whole human race depends are frequently taken as impulsive reactions, with emotional and prejudiced points of view, but all too seldom after methodical investigation of the basic facts, putting them together, checking them against all the sources of data available, and then carefully proceeding on the lines indicated.

Even at the governmental level we are seeing the beginnings of some improvement in this respect. For example, the hearings conducted by Senator Fulbright on Vietnam and on China are something that we have needed for a long time. We have people in this university, we have people in Cornell, we have people in all kinds of universities who have spent their lives learning everything it is possible for them to learn about South Vietnam and about China and about Southeast Asia. Why shouldn't we call on them? Why shouldn't we exploit everything they can tell us? That isn't difficult at all. We are beginning to do it. We are beginning to do it under the stimulation and under the leadership of Senator Fulbright, and if we pursue this kind of approach and if it is given more attention by the executive branch and by our society in general we will come out with some better answers to our problems.

MAN AND THE FUTURE | 6

HAS THE THEATER A FUTURE?

Harold Clurman

It may appear funny to some of you to ask, "Has the Theater a Future?" Obviously, the theater, like Britain, is going to stay forever, because the sense of play never leaves man as long as man is a man and not a computer. However, the question becomes more pertinent in view of certain facts.

New York has been the focal point of theatrical activity in this country for many, many years. In the theatrical season of 1899 and 1900 eighty-seven new productions were put on there. This number increased until 1926-27, when 264 productions were put on. In fact, one night, I think Christmas Eve of 1926, there were something like eleven productions put on, and the newspapers had to supplement their drama critics with people from the police department, Wall Street department, and other departments, some of whom were much better than the regular dramatic critics. True, they weren't professional; they just knew something about plays. In the thirties—which was a period of depression, as you know, or as you may have heard—all but one of the years had about a hundred productions put on. But in 1963-64 there were sixty-three plays put on, including musicals, comedies, etc. In other words, there were fewer productions in 1963-64, in a period of affluence so they tell me, than there were in 1899. In 1929 or '28 there were sixty theaters in New York. There are at present about thirty.

Now this diminishing number of productions, the shrinkage of productions in New York—and I do not speak about the equivalent and even more drastic shrinkage of road shows and stock companies all over the country—has been ascribed to many factors. The first everyone talks about is that radio is infringing upon the territory of the theater, that movies draw audiences away from the theater, that television at present draws audiences away from the theater. I am not altogether impressed with this particular reason, because in other countries where there is television the theater is still active to a degree that it isn't in this country. The theater in England is flourishing at the moment. In Germany the theater is very active; in fact there is a state theater, a municipal theater, in every city in Germany with more than 25,000 population. I never have believed one art necessarily eliminates the value of another. In other words, because we have movies we don't cease to look at paintings. Because we have paintings we don't cease to look at sculpture. Because we have music we don't cease to read books. Each of these arts has a life and validity of its own.

A more valid explanation, of course, is the economic explanation. The cost of production has mounted enormously I can tell you from my own experience. When I did a play called *Awake and Sing*, by Odets, which was the first play I ever directed myself, it cost something like $6,000 to produce a one-set play. Today that play would cost $75,000 to produce. As a consequence the cost of tickets has risen. When I first began to go to the theater you could sit in the orchestra for $2.50. Sometimes, in 1912, 1915, 1916, you could get a ticket in the orchestra for $2.00

at the best show, with fine actors, with John Barrymore, let's say. You could see a show for $1.50 on a Wednesday matinee, for $2.00 on a Saturday matinee; and there were fifty-cent seats, where I usually sat. Now there is no such thing as a fifty-cent seat. I think the minimum price in the orchestra for what they call a straight play, a play without music, is $6.90 in New York. At a musical it costs something like $9.00. If it is a particularly bad show it costs $12.00. Fewer people go to the theater as a consequence. And even the people who do go are what is popularly known in New York as the "expense account" audience, which is not exactly the most desirable audience to have. It is desirable in so far as they have money to pay.

This makes it imperative that all plays be smash hits. First of all, it takes six months or more to pay back the cost of a play. For example, a good play, like *Death of a Salesman* by Arthur Miller, with an interesting cast, with good notices, was sold out for six to eight months, much to the horror of the backers, before a single cent was retrieved. That was because the operating cost was so high. As a result, a play must almost automatically become a big hit. It must have at least four out of seven good notices. The critics must not only say it is a good play, it must be the greatest thing since electricity. It must be something that you would kill your neighbor to be able to see. Especially, it must be a play you can't dig up tickets for. If you can't get tickets for it, it is the most desirable play to see. This is very bad, because it so happens that some very good plays in the past and even today aren't smash hits. I passed by the theater when Shaw's *Arms and the Man* was first presented in London. I think it contained eighty seats and I'm not sure that they were all occupied, but Shaw seems to have made a reputation in spite of that. Recently two plays by Tennessee Williams were presented that got six or seven bad notices. The only exception to the bad notices was my own notice and I didn't think they were great plays; they left much to be desired, both in the script and the performance, but were new in a certain sense for Mr. Williams. They closed in a week. As I have often pointed out, nowadays we have the wonderful phenomena of plays that have run for one continuous performance. One of these was presented by a genius called David Susskind who once told me he had never had any failures. This was a play that ran for one continuous performance and cost $450,000. It is true that show business is no business.

All these things are very important factors in the crisis of the theater—if you want to call it that—but they don't seem to me to be the true cause. First of all, I realize that in the worst times of the Russian Revolution and of the French Revolution theaters were packed. Where there was very little money and very little to eat in Moscow there was a very charming production, which is still done, of a play called The Princess Turandot based on an eighteenth-century Italian play by Gozzi which had no politics at all. The audience came in shivering, hungry, to the theater, and enjoyed and loved that play. In fact, it encouraged the spectators, gave them hope that they would see a better day.

In this country we have, of course, a tradition, a puritan tradition, which is not merely a religious matter but an economic matter in the same sense that it took a long time for the theater to be established because the theater and all the other arts were not in the minds of the people. What was in the minds of the people was to build log cabins, to build roads, and later to build bridges and build all sorts of things. There was always some form of popular theater —the show boats, the minstrel shows after awhile, and you might say campfire shows that didn't pretend to be art but were expressions of desire to play; but it took a long time for the theater to establish itself anywhere but on the eastern seaboard. Even then only the wealthy, and the educated, which was a small group, came to see bowdlerized versions of Shakespeare. They were very surprising Shakespearean productions. Sometimes they were given happy endings. Mostly the actors came from England, sometimes from France. Edmund Kean got himself in trouble in Boston one day because he bawled out the audience for not being more numerous, after which they treated him as if he were a Bolshevik.

For a long time there was very little theater. Theatrical activity increased with our first American tragedian, Edwin Forest, who wrote and produced the first American play—it wasn't actually the first but it was what he called the first "real American" play, which meant that its hero was an Indian. He gave a prize; he was the first to give a prize for an American play. And he called himself an American actor so emphatically because of the contrast with English actors and French actors and others who had come. He even put an American flag on his program, so no one would mistake who he was or what he was. And when his rival from England came, McCready, there was a riot and people got killed, the partisans of one against the other. They took the theater quite seriously in those first days. I don't know if there was entertainment in the theater but outside it was marvelous.

The field became more and more prosperous as the country became rich and there was more desire to spread the benefits of culture and entertainment. During the early years of this century there were a number of extraordinarily good American actors although the plays were not so good. I think you could produce such plays now only to the absolute howling laughter of the audience.

There began to be road shows and stock companies and since it was the main form of entertainment—there was no radio, no television—the people attended the theater in great numbers. The theater became a business, and the theater always has to be a business to the degree that money is charged. There has to be administration; there has to be organization. However, I think that this factor, that it became a profitable business in a country where the business of the country is business, to quote an American president, caused the theater to become a show shop, a place where they sold stuff called shows. A play was a commodity you put on to make money, just as certain people say the reason you have razors is because there is a razor business, not because you need a shave. So the theater became a show shop for which material was sold. The material was sometimes good material, and good artists, very sincere people, were engaged in it. There is not necessarily a contradiction between making a profit on a show and making an excellent show. There was a show shop and plays and shows were the commodities, and what was back of it all was the idea that the theater is entertainment.

Now the theater is entertainment. It should be entertainment at all times. But when you say the theater is entertainment, you have said very little, because you haven't differentiated theater entertainment from a basketball game, or a baseball game, or a boxing match, or billiards, or ballroom dancing, or even less reputable entertainments. In order to know what you are talking about when you say the theater is entertainment, you must ask what sort of entertainment it is. How does it engage one; what does it engage?

And now I must define what the theater is. First of all, the source of the theater is the audience. That's where theater comes from. That produces the play. Because actors, even though sometime you won't believe it, have mothers and fathers and relatives, they grow up in a community, and they go to schools. They are in contact with the same things that we are in contact with. And they play and they become professionals. What do they play at? They tell us about ourselves. They enunciate what we are happy about, what we glory in, what we are proud of, what we truly believe, what we worry about, what our anguish is. In the old rituals dances had to do with the growth of corn or the bringing of rain because those things were essential to the life of the community. The theater is basically a communication which is at the same time a communion. It is a communication in the sense that certain people from the audience, mainly people who became professional playwrights, people who became professional actors or scenic artists and so forth, are communicating something that they want to say in common, that you will understand because they are part of you and you are part of them. They are glorifying some aspect of your and their lives; laughing at some of the pleasures you and they experience; inspiring themselves and you with desires, with hopes, even with religious beliefs, becoming aware. The theater is a means whereby a community realizes itself, knows that it has an identity, knows that it shares certain things. This can be done in the form of comedy, this can be done in the form of farce, this can be done in the form of musicals. It doesn't have to be, as we say, theater with a message. (By the way all plays have a message. Sometimes it has a message that says, "Aren't we a sorry lot?" But the audience doesn't necessarily know that is what is being said.)

The great message I remember of the twenties, when I came back after three years in Europe, was delivered in the Ziegfeld Follies. I saw a marvelous communication glorifying the American girl and I approved of that entirely. The Follies conveyed the message well; the girls were glorious to look at. But the show also bespoke the wealth that America represented, the beauty of the silks and satins, the good nature, the friendliness. Will Rogers and Eddie Cantor were the leading comedians, and they spoke of our well being, of our prosperity, the days when every garage would have hundreds of chickens and every park hundreds of automobiles.

Every play speaks to me. I have never yet seen a play— sometimes rather dumb, sometimes stuttering—that does not tell me something, about the actors, about the audience, about my life. If it doesn't say any of those things, or says very little, then I am unentertained; in other words, I am not engaged. To be entertained is to be engaged. When I go to the theater I want to be completely engaged in my senses and in my mind, in my heart. I want to be physically moved. I want to be mentally excited. I want to be spiritually elevated. Then I am really entertained. And so Hamlet can become a vividly entertaining show (under certain circumstances Hamlet can become a big bore), whereas certain comedies make me weep. Goethe went to a show in Venice and noted: "I went to a tragedy and never laughed so much in my life." This is all history I am telling you and also a matter of current knowledge. What were the Greeks doing in their theater that was to do so much for us? Aeschylus, Sophocles, and those fellows, what were they doing? They were enunciating their view of life, their religion, their pride. They were talking about themselves. It was a ritual in which the whole community took part.

Even in the Middle Ages, when the church frowned on the idea of play acting, the desire for theater, the need for theater, the value of theater were recognized. We had elaborate morality plays in which almost the whole town took part because the sets were built by the guilds, the costumes were made by the guilds, and they were very elaborate and some horribly realistic. The church adopted the theater to educate many illiterate people as to the nature of Christianity, its glory, its fears, and its triumphs. And we know about the English court support of the Elizabethan theater, which, by the way, was the first modern commercial theater. The English court (Elizabeth and others) brought people in to act. The nobles protected some of the actors because there was a puritanical segment of the population opposed to the theater; they thought it was immoral. At the French court, Louis XIV was proud of Racine and Moliere. Sometimes he said, "You are going a bit too far in your propaganda, you are getting a little out of hand, especially when you produce a play like *Tartuffe*, which my mistress doesn't like; she is very religious." All royalty felt that plays were a part of the patrimony of the country. That was what France meant to a Frenchman—seeing the Racine, the Moliere plays. There were disputes about them among those who could read and those who could go to the theater, a very small part of the population. Even Napoleon, when he made that unnecessary trip to Moscow, took pains in the midst of all his troubles to issue rules for the Comédie Française back in Paris. He ordered that there be no balcony tickets costing more than five francs. He was concerned about what was going on not only in political or military affairs but in the theater, as part of French culture. This was part of what France was and is. Our culture is what we are. It is not an hors d'oeuvre; it is not an aperitif. It is the main function of man to express himself. The theater happens to be a very vital and living form of expression because it includes all the arts and is created in the immediate presence of the living community. So the theater becomes the consciousness of the public.

Now in order to have a good theater you have to have a good audience. Not that the audience educates the theater or the theater educates the audience. Both happen at the same time. I would say that one of the things that has happened in connection with the shrinkage of the Broadway theater is that the audience has become a rather routine audience. The audience can't become a democratic audience in the precise sense of the term because it excludes too many people. A public school teacher in New York City can hardly afford to go to the theater. It is hard to get to the theater. He has to go into this horrible New York subway. If he has to have a taxi, which is expensive, that is a hazard, too. The taxicab driver himself is a hazard.

I have had a definite experience with this routine audience. I have suffered from it and I have enjoyed it. The critics come to the theater and get out about 10:15. If you go to the middle of town, to Sardi's, the people there are already reading their reviews at midnight. And when the boxoffice opens at 10 o'clock on the day after opening night you see a long line if the notices have been good; if the New York *Times* notice and the *Tribune* notice have been good the line is even longer. (They rarely agree for some reason. It is as though they have an agreement not to agree.) These lines are particularly noticeable should it happen that both notices have been good, for example, if they say "The show is a thunderbolt!" This is a deep critical insight, by the way. I put on a play called A *Touch of the Poet*, a very serious play by a serious writer. It was highly praised; one critic called it a "thunderbolt." I said, "My God, if I read that I would stay as far away from that play as possible because I don't particularly like thunderbolts." Another critic said, "It's terribly exciting." Such are the deep insights we get from most of our critics. Stendhal makes a wonderful observation in one of his novels. He pointed out that if you went to a concert and somebody shot a gun, the gun would be far more exciting than Mozart, but it wouldn't be music. So if the play is as "exciting as a thunderbolt," or if "you fall down laughing," or "you break your ribs laughing," or "you must not miss it," or "you won't be anybody if you don't see it," or something really perceptive like that, you will see the audience, the ticket buyers, with the *Times* hot in their hands, still reading the thing trying to get to that darned boxoffice. Half their lives would be wasted if they aren't able to say, "I have just seen the greatest show that ever was." If it is a comedy the audience comes in laughing at the ushers.

There is no individual thinking. Of course, these are very broad statements. You, of course, all do think when you go to the theater! I'll never forget seeing *Mr. Roberts*. It got marvelous notices; it was an entertaining show. An actor came in and he spat into a rubber plant and there was a howl. The audience laughed because they had been told it was funny. The play is a condiment. It is a sauce. (By the way, I love low comedy. It is very healthy, very hygienic!) All plays don't have to be high tragedy. When a girl on the stage is very pretty I always note it; people say one of the reasons I go to the theater is to see pretty girls. I like to see them other places, too, but it is sort of pleasant, when the play is bad, for there at least to be one pretty girl on the stage!

The audience has become routine and without knowing it critics have too. They are not bad fellows; most of them are nice guys. Most of them learn about the theater as they go to it. Some of them have a knowledge of the theater that goes back at least ten years. One or two of them have been seen to read a book. But I have not seen any of them at a concert or at an art gallery.

We have to educate the public—there are many ways of doing it—and then the critics will be educated. Since the economic pressure of the routine which I described applies to us all, we all fall into line. We achieve a pattern of behavior which makes us think superficially, no matter how we try to avoid it. The general atmosphere dictates. The critics are really not responsible for the situation. The play is supposed to be news; therefore you have to get the review in half an hour or fifty minutes after the last curtain has fallen.

There are ways of educating the public. There are ways of talking to them: meetings and newspapers and articles, books, and the theaters themselves if there were theaters which were established, permanent institutions instead of show shops. The theater itself would make propaganda for itself, not only to get people to come to the show but also to explain what this show is all about—what the author is trying to do, who the author is. For example, when you go to Jean Louis Berrault's Theatre de France in Paris and see a film by Giraudoux, you find out what Claudel thought, you learn what Catholic critics thought, you read the history of Giraudoux's career. You are instructed; you are informed. You are not told to like it or to dislike it. You are given a background. The play becomes part of the cultural context of the nation. You see that the play is not an isolated little thing to titillate one or to make one cry but part of a general statement made by a serious writer.

When I travel I always go to a theater, not because I am a theater man but because I want to find out what is going on in the country I visit. I go to the theater because, somehow, through the audience and its reception of the play, through criticism of it, I know what is going on in the country at the moment. It is much more revealing than reading the local newspaper. For example, I happened to be present at the opening night in London of *Look Back in Anger*. I found faults in the play but I felt that it expressed a new England, that England had changed since the war. I felt that there was a new beat, social and political. The plays that the French wrote in the fifties are called the "Theater of the Absurd," which is an absurd name for them. From these pessimistic plays I understood the despair of the country, the sense of helplessness due to their bad experiences during the war, which caused people to become apolitical, anxious to get away from all types of political discussion. I saw the plays as fundamentally plays of protest against a world which the authors could no longer believe in and trust.

So to come to the main issue again. I feel there is no future in the theater as it now is constituted on Broadway. That doesn't mean that there will be no good writers for it. It doesn't mean that all actors will expire, although I know that some actors who study very seriously—voice lessons, speech lessons, body lessons, and the history of the theater— will end up selling beer on television shows. This is not a very happy outcome for a long career devoted to preparing yourself for the acting profession. This theater will still, as it does now, produce some very entertaining, very pleas- ant musical comedies and light comedies and occasionally a serious play. I just feel that because the theater as a business is failing as a business it cannot have a future. Therefore I hold out little hope for New York theater as now constituted.

Of course, the crisis sometimes provokes or brings about its remedy. Sometimes the disease makes the necessity of a cure more pressing and therefore sometimes it is found. And I do feel there is a future for theater—for a new theater. The first cause for this will not be because an angelic person declares, "Let's have a nice theater." The cause will be the very need for the theater, the very appetite for the theater, which has not died out. I have been all through the coun- try: the desire for a living theater, a theater with "round actors," has not died out. The prevalent unrest of youth that we hear about today, this quest for some value, some truth, something to hang on to, takes many forms. It takes political forms, it sometimes takes the form of chaotic behavior and chaotic thinking about political matters. Definitely there is a desire to say, "Let's get something done, let's see different plays, let's see outrageous plays, let's see mad plays, but let's see something that isn't just complacent, just conformist."

As a result, all over the country, both in universities and in small towns, permanent theaters are being established, not only by amateur actors, and semi-amateur actors, but by professionals. Very often actors finally come to this same conclusion that I have, and some directors say, "I will not have anything to do with Broadway. I am going to Pittsburgh, I am going to New Orleans, I am going to go anywhere I can do the plays I want the way I want them in front of an audience to whom these plays will be as manna from heaven." And so theaters are cropping up all over. We read about the theater in Minneapolis, which is one of the most notable because of its very important and fine director. But similar theaters are being created as well in Seattle and San Francisco. Cornell University is putting up a professional theater under Allan Schneider, who is a successful Broadway director. Such people sometimes spend six months or more in small towns and try to establish theater schools there. They go on speaking to people, in schools and clubs and public forums and colleges wherever they can gather to explain the theater, to make the theater more vivid, more alive, and—to get a little more profound— to explain the pertinent nature of plays.

New critics will develop. People ask me what a critic should do. I don't think a critic is a good critic because he says a play is good and I agree with him or he is a bad critic because I don't agree with him. What I want a critic to do if he likes or dislikes the play is to illuminate the play for me, to make me see its relationship to the world, to make me see the kind of spirit the author represents, the kind of world view that he represents. There have been reviews of this kind. For example, if you read, and I hope you will if you are interested in the theater, Mr. Shaw's mistaken views on *The Importance of Being Earnest*, by Oscar Wilde, you will find Shaw thought less well of *The Importance of Being Earnest* than of *An Ideal Husband*, an inferior play. It doesn't matter; it's a marvelous review. I don't agree with him, he has been proved wrong by time, but in the course of that review he says certain things about farce which are extremely pertinent today and for all time, because Shaw had a mind, a point of view, a philosophy—because he was Shaw! By the way, a critic should be an interesting man in the same way an artist is an interesting man.

Although I speak of a new development I don't think we are likely to achieve Utopia because of it. Houston, Texas, has been granted two million dollars to build a new theater but money alone won't solve the problem. What is important is that this is one of the signs of the times. New theater buildings are going up so fast and in so many places that I have come to call it the "edifice complex." Many are marvelous buildings, but I say, "What are you putting in them, what is your aim, what are you going to say in the new theater?" When I do a play I think, "This thing must in some way communicate an idea dear to the audience because I got the idea *from the audience. I got the idea from living in the community.*"

The development will be slow: there will be a lot of eclecticism, artiness; there will be a lot of kidding around with styles. Style is a particular way of seeing things and therefore a particular way of expressing things. We know that some of these theaters will fail, they will disappoint the public, they will probably do plays that don't fit the audience.

In fifteen years you will see a better American theater than you see today. There will be mistakes and faltering and we will all give up in despair, because the American people are notoriously impatient people. Our idea that everything can be done in a minute, that everything must and can be immediately remedied, is a part of our lack of cultural stamina. Educating the public is a hard job. It is a hard job to transform a culture which in many ways is pulling another way. Every culture has its duality. There is the regressive and there is the progressive.

I want a new theater. I think it is going to come and I have told you how it might come. It will articulate ideas which will move us, which will touch us, stir us, arouse us, anger us, and exalt us. In any case, what it will do is help to make us more human than we are and to have more fun. The greatest fun comes not from having "fun," but from being thoroughly human.

COMMENTARIES

LARRABEE: As a lapsed theatergoer I can offer only a personal attempt to describe why I don't go anymore. I am one of the people who have given it up, and for reasons that only in part are the ones Mr. Clurman was talking about. I would like to put forward a couple of them by way of explaining what

I think is wrong with the theater, and why it is in as perilous
a state as Mr. Clurman described. The first is a complaint as
to substance. If the audience is the creator of what goes on
much of the modern stage, then the audience—even if it is just
that Sardi's first-night, expense account audience—must be
possessed of some strange craving for violence, for meaningless
violence, violence for its own sake, what a friend of mine calls
"pansy-violence," homosexual violence. One gets the feeling
that the audience goes to be shocked. When it is said of a play,
as it is said by these telegraphic critics, "moving, powerful
drama," or some other such phrase, what it often turns out
to mean is that the audience has been clobbered by the playwright, who has indulged his control over the play and over
the actors simply to rig the machinery of the stage, to throw in
violence simply for its shock affect.

I should be specific about this because obviously sadism of
itself or murder or incest or other unspeakable crimes have not
been forbidden topics. Certainly Shakespeare is full of them.
But there is a difference today, and the difference seems to me
to be the self-indulgence of the playwright and the manipulation
of the audience. I call it homosexual because of the traditional
clinical association of sadism with homosexuality, which Stekel
and other psychoanalysts commented on, and the persistent
theme of hatred for women which shows up in many of the
same playwrights. If I can give you another example outside of the
theater I would pick the conspicuous phenomenon today of
Capote's *In Cold Blood*. You may have seen Kenneth Tynan's
criticism of Capote for failing, so Tynan thinks, to do more to
save these two murderers from their fate. I must say I think
Tynan is completely missing the point. The point of the book
seems to me to be that this decent, bourgeois, in-every-way-
irreproachable family represents everything that Truman Capote
hates, and if those two screwballs hadn't killed them then he
would have had to do it himself.

The effect of this on myself as a member of the audience is
one of extreme distaste and a feeling of being had. It isn't
a matter of disagreeing with the philosophy; it's a matter of
what one allows the playwright to get away with. And I feel
they are getting away with more than murder.

The second complaint is a matter of technique: brutally, and put in exaggerated form, many actors simply do not know how to act. Incidentally, great experiences for me in the theater recently have all been French. The experiences had a great deal to do with technique. The first was Marcel Marceau, for the overpoweringly rewarding experience of being returned to the essentials of the theater. Marceau makes you realize that the theater is a board, a stage, and a man on it. And starting with that alone he does magic and returns you to the essentials. The second was the Jean Louis Barrault production of *Christophe Colomb* in which this choreographic quality was extended to the whole cast so you felt there was hardly a motion being made on the stage that wasn't disciplined in thought and carefully considered. The third was another French performance. I went up to a little theater in Montmartre and saw Turgenev's *Day in the Country* done by a repertory company, and there was an overpowering contrast to a New York theater production in the way the cast was acting together. They were not a group of separate talents each trying to steal the stage from the other. Again they were choreographed in a disciplined, trained, and enormously effective sense.

Now the word usually put on the inability of American actors to act is the term "method," which I think is exaggerated. It describes a school of acting which supposes that what you feel can make up for what you don't know professionally. There is a director on the Broadway stage named George Abbott, who directs all those ephemeral musical comedies Mr. Clurman secretly goes to. There are stories told of how Abbott deals with "method" actors. One is about an actor who came to a point in rehearsal and said, "What am I supposed to be thinking about during this scene?" Abbott said, "Your job." On another occasion the actor had been changing his part and Abbott remonstrated with him, and the actor said, "I am terribly sorry but this is the way I feel it." And Abbott said, "Okay." There was one scene in the play where the actor was alone on the stage and there was a spotlight on him, and the next day when he started his speech the spotlight moved away, and the actor very angrily came up to Abbott afterwards and said, "What's with that electrician?" And Abbott said, "Well, I tell you, I have been talking to him and he just doesn't feel it that way."

One difficulty with us, in contrast to the elegant European productions, is of course the matter of financial support. I am sure Mr. Clurman was thinking a great deal of the time, though he didn't say so, about the fact that these European theaters are subsidized. One of the reasons the tickets are so inexpensive, and so many ordinary folk can go to the performances, is that the costs are being paid by the state. Barrault's theater, Jean Vilar's Theatre National Populaire, or the Comedie Française, or the Opera Comique, are all subsidized by the state, just as in Britain. The British Arts Council supports theaters, as well as opera and ballet. Stupefyingly, Germany, a few years ago, in a supremely contemptuous gesture, gave a few million dollars to our own Lincoln Center.

In that sense I certainly agree with Mr. Clurman that the fact that the theater is dying economically has something to do with its vitality, that it can't be saved artificially, that it's got to find another way back. And certainly the ways it has been finding recently have come from the small theaters, the off-Broadway theaters, and from the small theaters around the rest of the country where new energies are developing. It's always been a sad thing in this country that we haven't had repertory. It has never taken root here and people time and again have pled for it and wondered why we don't have it. In New York now, for instance, a repertory theater is trying to get started in Lincoln Center, but it needs a school along with it. When Lincoln Kristen saved American ballet he saved it with a school, by training dancers, starting with the very young. I would suspect that to make a repertory theater possible the same thing has got to be done in theater to develop people who are really professionally competent in the various classical styles.

SHAYON: Mr. Clurman is a man who illuminates the contemporary situation of the theater. I echo his hope that the renaissance that he wants so passionately and urges upon all of us will come about, but I suspect that it won't. I think the future of the theater in western civilization is that of a beautiful museum piece. I think the theater of the living stage has become irrelevant on several counts. One, it has become irrelevant to audiences who no longer bring to the theater their own passionate concerns. The theater today, for Broadway

audiences, even for touring company audiences, is two hours
of distraction. They come into the theater and they enjoy
what they find; they may laugh, they may weep, but when they
go out, it's forgotten; the slate is wiped clean. The theater
that we inherited from classic times was one that had profound
relevance to the religious, social, and political aspects of
community experience. Today, theater has lost that relevance
in our lives, and I don't think a theater based on distraction,
however charming, however beautifully done, can ever be more
than a museum piece. I think also that theater has become
irrelevant to the actor, the producer, the writer—the people
who make theater. Historically, these people have gone
"where the action is." The action today is where the largest
audiences are. The stage flourished at a time when audiences
came to theaters. Today, technology has given us new ways
of reaching greater audiences that pay greater financial rewards
to the artists. Actors, writers, and producers may take theater
courses in universities but they generally dream of going to
Hollywood or breaking into television and becoming vice-
presidents of networks. The talent, which a community gen-
erates, will inevitably, in the absence of any other controls but
those of the market place, tend to gravitate to areas that offer
the larger marginal returns. And this brings us to the institutional configuration under which our society gets its "theater,"
which is its leisure experience. It has come to be the electronic
stage.

Cecil B. De Mille once prophesied that motion pictures
would eventually be shown in homes; the boxoffice would be
the home. His prophecy is coming true—the electronic
configuration, the absorption of ideas in the atmosphere of the
home, rather than in the ritual atmosphere of a darkened temple.
The absorption of information and ideas as part of a contextual
process where they are only part of the ideas we are taking into
our consciousness is coming to be the dominant pattern of
our society. When you stop to think that the average American
family presumably watches television between five and six hours
per day, you begin to get some sense of what profound
implications the technological revolution in communicating
ideas is having on society. The attention of our people is being
bid for by powerful forces. The theater cannot prosper; it does

not have the energy, the vitality, the talent to bid for that attention. The big networks, the big capital suppliers, do have the energy and the money and the talent to bid for that attention.

Some of you may have noticed that the CBS network is going into the production of feature pictures. The network has already produced *My Fair Lady*, which it owns. All the networks, faced by a sparsity of programs, are now entering the field of film production and are financing features. Every aspect of the conveyance of leisure entertainment is being gobbled up by the enormous maw of the commercial enterprise. Through radio, television, and movies, it's the theater that comes to us, not the theater to which we go. And if we are concerned about the future of the living theater, I think we are romantic. I belong to that school which looks back to the theater that we have inherited from western civilization. I think the theater of the future is going to ignore it. And if we want to have some kind of impact, if we want to bridge the journey into the future and carry over with us some of the great human impulses which we have inherited from the theater as it has existed in the past, we had better begin to pay serious attention to the cultural, to the institutional arrangements by which we and our children are going to absorb the theater in the future.

MONTAGU: It seems the theater has lived to see the funeral of its own reputation. When Mr. Shayon made his remarks I couldn't help but confirm them from my own experience and the experience of those who have investigated the matter, among them Mr. Shayon. At the same time I found myself in virtually complete agreement with Mr. Clurman and with Mr. Larrabee. But as an anthropologist who has had, as one of his eccentric hobbies, an interest in the theater and in reading plays, I must confess that I have seen, I know, as a student of the ethos of the time as exhibited in these plays from the earliest days on, largely beginning with Greek plays and going through the Roman theater down to our own time, that the theater has an extremely important role to play in every society. Because from my own experience in teasing out the contribution the theater has made to humanity, the theater, I have found, has always been in the vanguard of new ideas and

220 | *Commentaries*

has been indeed a revolutionary force in every society in which
it has acted as critic and social commentator—as well as entertainment. Hence I would place the theater very high in the
hierarchy of social institutions. I therefore make a very strong
plea for the citizenry, through its government, to recognize this
and institute, as is being done in other countries, a national
theater, in which every state has theater supported by the federal
government and by the state and in which the government
plays no more role than that. It should not have a word to
say as to what plays shall be produced or how they shall be
produced or whether they shall be produced or whether they
shall be censored.

As you know, England has started a national theater very
recently to which Kenneth Tynan, a brilliant man to whom
reference already has been made, has been appointed. The
national theater was started with the firm conviction on the
part of everyone, and as Kenneth Tynan said again and again,
that there would not be a completely satisfactory attendance
at these plays of this national theater at the beginning. The
fact is that 100 per cent attendance has been the record for
every play. In fact they haven't been able to meet the demands.
And I don't see why the richest country in the world could not
do as much for the theater. I would make a very strong plea
for a federal national theater and for, of course, a state theater,
and I would also say that when Mr. Clurman said that there
was little hope for the New York theater as presently
constituted I rather think that he meant to say the Broadway
theater as presently constituted, because some of the very
finest things that have been produced in any country have
been produced in off-Broadway theaters, little stalls converted
into theaters, restaurants converted into theaters, even ware-
houses, where I have seen the most magnificent plays and where
the contribution has been a very considerable one. The trouble
with Broadway is and will always remain that the principal
criterion of success is the boxoffice, and so long as this is so
a really good play can only appear in New York on Broadway
by pure accident.

CLURMAN: I have very little to add. I have been corrected
and well corrected, about the off-Broadway theater. I could

go into all aspects of the question but I am happy that Mr. Montagu mentioned off-Broadway theater where the plays of Pinter, Genêt, and other important new writers have been presented. I also am happy that Mr. Montagu has emphasized the value of a subsidized theater. We must have more than one national theater, we must have a state theater, we might have municipal theaters.

I once was asked, "Are you in favor of having a subsidized theater?" and I said, "First let's have it and then we can attack it." When good theater comes I won't be satisfied. I will still be criticizing it because that is part of the creation of further developments.

As to the disappearance of theater, Mr. Shayon is repeating what I have said. He just describes the disease in another way. But he offers us a solution: television, electronics. I have nothing against television or electronics. Most of the stuff they offer us is infantile at the moment but that doesn't mean it must always be so. But I must say that Mr. Shayon speaks within a very narrow context. In London's British National Theater, you can't get a seat to see *Othello* or to see any of the modern plays. The theaters there are well attended even though people also watch television.

If you are talking simply in terms of numbers, that is a different story; I am not absolutely sure that things that appeal to fifty million people instead of a smaller number are necessarily better for the people. In Germany theaters are crowded and they also love opera. They have a tradition that is not concerned merely with numbers. As for the statement that the theater has to come to the people, it makes me feel that the next time a girl friend calls me up I am going to say, "Listen, you are absolutely superannuated and love is superannuated because I don't want to go to you like I used to do in the old days; you have to come to me because I am watching television."

SHAYON: For those of you who occasionally read my *Saturday Review* column, as well as go to the living theater, you know that Mr. Clurman has pushed me into a corner which I will not accept. My position is not that I am offering electronic communication as a remedy. I deplore the phenomenon which is taking place. I am merely stating that all our passionate dedication to our ideals does not necessarily mean that this is the way it will come about. I am in favor of the national theater, I am in favor of a pluralistic sampling of all kinds of theatrical experiences, but I warn you that the theater in this country has always been an experience for a small elite. We do not have the traditions that exist in homogeneous European countries. We are a big sprawling country. We have heterogeneous racial strains and intellectual traditions. We are anti-intellectual in our approach to the theater. Why has there never been a successfully anthology program on television? Precisely because there is no anthology tradition in the American experience. There is such a tradition in European experience. What I am saying is that whether we like it or not, and I don't like it, the main stream of theatrical experience in this country is coming to be more and more through the electronic media. I say we must fight it. We must fight it, among other ways, by a renaissance of small theaters in local communities. But I am not so sure that we will win the fight. I wish you luck.

MONTAGU: I would like to transmit to you a discovery I made in Shakespeare concerning what we have been talking about here, with particular reference to television. In the first act of *Romeo and Juliet*, in the first scene one of the characters speaks in such a way that there is no doubt whatsoever that Shakespeare had television in mind. He has his character say, "But soft, what light through yonder window breaks, it speaks and yet says nothing?"

MAN AND THE FUTURE | 7

OUR CRIMES AGAINST CRIMINALS:
A PLEA

Karl Menninger

As long as I can remember I have had a compulsion to brag about Kansas, and if there was something about our state that wasn't quite right I wanted to improve it. When I went away to college, my classmates nicknamed me "Kansas," because I talked so much about our weather, our natural beauties, geographic advantages, culture, and universities. Some of my fellow citizens had an inferiority feeling about Kansas. I thought we ought to overcome that, and I resolved to do what I could to help my native state when the time came.

But I became absorbed in new discoveries in medicine, and especially the treatment of mental illness. I forgot about Kansas for awhile. Then my chief died. He was one of the great inspirations of my life, next to my parents, the finest teacher I ever had. His death changed my life in many ways, because he had said, "Go back to your own people. You know them; they'll listen to you. They are open minded—more so than our people here in the East." And I did.

Kansas welcomed me back and helped me, my father, and later my brother. We tried to demonstrate in a small way that the mentally ill can be cured. That was the gospel in those days: "good news." The mentally ill could be cured—yes, if they could afford it, if they could obtain the proper help promptly. Many couldn't. But people didn't believe it.

Then in 1945 the Veterans Administration decided, "Whether we can afford it or not, we want our veterans, our ex-soldiers, to have the best." They proceeded to establish the remarkable Veterans Administration hospital chain, with our hospital here in Kansas as the pilot, placing particular emphasis on the treatment of the mentally ill. Three years later Governor Carlson, his legislature, and the people of Kansas, proclaimed, "We want all our people to have what the veterans have. We want the best. Can we have it?"

We didn't have it. We were next to the bottom among the forty-eight states with respect to the adequacy of our care of the mentally ill. There are a lot of states I would have thought would be worse than we; but there was only one. (I won't tell you which one.)

Governor Carlson appointed the then dean of the Medical School, Dr. Franklin Murphy, and a few others of us to form a committee. We made a study of the state hospital system and of the mentally ill who were consigned to the care of the state, and we drew up a blueprint for making the system better. We received excellent support from the news media, the press, radio and television, as well as from the legislature, and from our very responsive Kansas population.

Those wonderful people of Kansas. We ought all to be proud of them. They said, "We want the best that can be had for our people," and they provided it. In 1948 Kansas rose from forty-seventh to first place in the nation in its provision for the mentally ill, and has stayed there ever since, during various political administrations. The care of the mentally ill has, thank heaven, ceased to be a political question in our state.

This University has had a big part in giving Kansas that pre-eminence. There is education going on here, in Manhattan, Wichita, Kansas City, and many places over our state. Education is a program of somewhat older, somewhat more experienced individuals helping somewhat less experienced or knowledgeable people. This is what we are engaged in; this is what we are celebrating in this centennial. Education is going on *also* at our state mental hospitals, at Osawatomie, at Larned, in Topeka, and in Kansas City; education for individuals who also receive help from some more experienced and maybe a little more stable or more fortunate than they. And the results are good. Do you know how good? Do you know that about 90 per cent "graduate" within three months of admission? I don't know whether most people realize it, but this is true.

There is a third type of institutional education provided by the state of Kansas and also by the federal government in Kansas. In a community just north of here there are nearly as many "students" as there are here in Lawrence. I am referring to the several prisons located there. That is a kind of education, too. Is it the right kind of education?

In my hand I hold a weapon, a heavy iron bar with a crook at the end, which was one of the instruments of education used in one of these institutions in a sister state. This iron bar was used not only to hit people on the head or the back, but also to communicate with the people who were being educated, to whom the guards were not permitted to speak. Two raps on the floor might mean, "Go to your cells." Three raps, "Head for the dining room," or something of the sort. That was the message; this club was the medium. Yet those institutions aimed at achieving a change in human beings such as a teacher hopes to effect his students. They hoped to point to a better way.

The "graduates" of such institutions will come back into the population of Kansas; they will once more be a part of our body politic. They will contribute something of what they have learned. Will they help the community go, and make the world better and keep themselves self-supporting?

How successful are we in this type of education in our state? Are we correcting error and instilling purpose? Or are we repeating the snake-pit horrors of frustration and neglect which used to characterize our state hospitals and still characterize state hospitals in many states?"

"Once insane always insane"; that's what Dr. Wescoe, Dr. Murphy, and I used to hear from a few men who needed enlightenment. Nobody believes that slanderous, ignorant canard any more. We have almost done away with the word "insane." We certainly have almost done away with the stigmatization of people who are sensible enough to go for help when they need it, instead of pretending that they don't.

How about "once a criminal always a criminal"? Do you believe *that*? Is it true? Is it partially true in this state? I think it is partially true in other states. Why? For the same reason "once insane always insane" was also once partially true. Untold numbers of people who were mentally ill never became well because they weren't given an opportunity to get well. They were never expected to get well. They were never helped to get well. They were treated as if they were hopeless and they became hopeless. I submit that we do the same thing with many legal offenders. Kansas is far behind in this field, the whole United States is far behind, as a matter of fact; far behind the advances of many other countries.

To begin with, the whole arrest-trial-sentence-punishment system is an antiquated, obsolescent rigamarole. Leading lawyers and judges all over the country are trying to change it. They are committed constitutionally to doing everything with extreme slowness and thoroughness so that to some of us it seems interminable, but they are taking some steps. Here and there improvements are being made.

One of the factors that blocks progress is the barbarous monstrosity of capital punishment, which has been abolished in most civilized countries for a century. *De facto,* it has been abolished in the United States; executions have fallen steadily from several hundred a year, to one hundred, to seventy-five, to fifty, to twenty, until last year there were only seven executions. (Four of those seven were here in our own state.) This is absurd. Nobody wants to execute people. Nobody thinks it helps anything. Nobody believes it is other than a most antiquated, medieval provision, which is almost extinct. Yet it stays on the statute books as a stipulation and hence, all over the country, even in states which don't employ capital punishment, they must first *exempt* the individual from capital punishment, and after much fireworks the issue is properly laid to rest and the trial can go on. But this delayed trial is expensive and raises some ridiculous nonsense about the "degree of impaired responsibility." Is the criminal really intelligent enough to be executed? Is he healthy enough to be hanged? We don't want to hang anybody that isn't in good health. We don't mind hanging somebody that is a little stupid, but if he is slightly feeble-minded, of course, we wouldn't hang him! We want good, healthy people to hang.

Even when we shall have disposed of this anachronism, there will remain a system of criminal justice which involves the arrest, examination, detention, trial, defense, conviction, punishment, and parole of offenders which is antiquated, inefficient, and unscientific. It is so bad that it produces more crime than it prevents. Beginning with the difficulties of the understaffed, underpaid police forces in every city, attempting among many other duties to deal with the persistent manifestations of violence, one can proceed to the overcrowded courts. Ninety per cent of the offenders are not even apprehended; of those apprehended 90 per cent are never tried! Our jails and prisons are filled with offenders, most of them repeaters. Over and over they revolve, and are processed again and again. Most of them can be regarded as failures in the crime business; the successful ones have eluded capture. The judicial system is a near scandal, and leading jurists, from whom I obtain most of my information, are doing their best to find ways of improving it.

President Johnson recently appointed a National Crime Commission, which I have had the honor to assist. A lot of things are being done, most important among these the attempt to educate the public about where we stand in the matter. That is what I am trying to do here, also. The most striking problem about the criminal and our treatment of him is that the public doesn't know the basic facts. People pick up their papers and learn that somebody, somewhere, has done something scandalous. "Oh, I want to read all about this! I want to see what happened. Did they catch him? What did they do with him?" It's like a fairy tale: a terrible man-eating giant has been captured somewhere. The incident has been blown up into a kind of drama. Every day thousands of people transgress the line of legality, do something they shouldn't, among them you and I. Some of them do pretty serious things; some (but few) of them get caught; and some of them have to be dealt with. They are dealt with according to a definite ritual.

If you don't happen to have affluent relatives, or good

friends, or belong to a fraternity with a large bank account, all you have to do to obtain free room and board is pass a forged check. The state will immediately provide you with room and board and indefinite detention. Do you believe that this cures people of writing bad checks? To do so isn't even a crime in Europe; it's a peculiarity of our legal system. But one thing which all Americans seem to think particularly dreadful is putting the wrong name on a piece of paper, or putting too large a number in the upper right hand corner. Some people under the influence of desperation or maybe a little alcohol, or perhaps just kidding themselves think they will deposit some money tomorrow. Then the check. Then the arrest. Then the trial, etc. How do we cure a man of this propensity, of committing this childish, wrong, dishonest act? Why, we put him in the penitentiary for a few years.

Now think about it—is there anything scientific about that? He can't be taught *not* to write in the penitentiary. He may learn to write, but he will not learn not to write. The penitentiary doesn't teach people that kind of thing. The whole procedure doesn't make any sense. The public is vastly apathetic about it. Tell them the system wastes money, and people shrug their shoulders. Tell them we are wasting human lives, and they repeat the gesture. Tell them we are committing crimes against criminals; no one weeps. Tell them we are committing crimes against ourselves by manufacturing more criminals; only a few believe it.

The first wrong we commit in this situation involves categorization. I refer to the victims of the system as offenders; most people will think of them as criminals. Suppose we are watching this fine orchestra here and you see some pretty girls playing the violin. You might say, "They are violinists." But I say, "Don't be ridiculous; they are **not** violinists—they are Methodists"—or Presbyterians, or majors in English, or somebody's most beautiful sweetheart, or some mother and father's darling. They are all kinds of things beside being violinists; if I just pin the label "violinists" on them, the girls will suffer. You don't want a date with a violinist, you want a date with a girl!

We shouldn't label anybody a criminal. Crime isn't the only thing about him, you know; it isn't the only thing he has done. Of course, you don't want a date with a criminal, but you might want to date or be friends with a man who has made a serious mistake and is pretty sorry about it, has corrected it, and is a lot better off now than some of us because he has learned about his shortcomings. He might be quite a person.

I am talking about the offenders that get caught; most of them are failures; most of them are poor; they are mostly black, or brown, tuberculous or otherwise physically afflicted. Why? Most of them are lonely, ostracized, homeless, friendless individuals. Why, do you suppose? Whatever the reason, we stigmatize them. We stamp them, as the Germans did the Jews during World War II, with a yellow badge: "Avoid these people!"

This is too bad, you say—a sorry situation, but why bring it up here? We are celebrating the one hundredth anniversary of a great training institution. We are training the fortunate ones, the promising ones. We can't be bothered with all those unlucky guys, those misfits, those failures. What is it to us?

I say it is *everything* to us. At the very heart of education is the idea that no man is an island, and that the bell tolls for you. And you and I are in the penitentiary business, whether we know it or not. We put offenders there. We keep them there. What can we do to make them emerge better than when they went in? What do I propose? I am going to propose, to the extent that educational and the scientific method can influence you, that we dispense with all the old trash about punishment or revenge being necessary. Vengeance is fine—in Verdi's operas, in *Othello* and in *Il Trovatore*. But the Hatfield-McCoy principle ought to die out among educated people after awhile. We say, "Turn the other cheek." If a man takes our coat, we give him the whole suit. "Vengeance is mine, saith the Lord, I will repay." Only we are afraid the Lord will not get around to it soon enough, so we take a little of the responsibility off His shoulders.

The fact that a man is poor when he steals a loaf of bread doesn't excuse him from the charge of larceny. The fact that a man is near naked and shivering when he steals an overcoat is no protection from being jailed as a thief. The fact that a man is frantic with panic or frustrated with rage when he swings the club is no excuse from the charge of murder.

Maybe—you think—the fact that he is frenzied or confused or hallucinated might get him off. Maybe the poor devil, though he is an awful fellow, just can't help it. But you psychiatrists want to call everybody sick. You want to eliminate public vengeance and punishment for all these fellows. Why, they ought to get their deserts!

Yes, we do want to eliminate vengeance and punishment. But we do not say that all offenders are sick. We say that there is something wrong with them and the fact that they continue to go about their silly, erroneous way of living is proof of it. It is a bit crazy to go slashing around, hurting other people. Stealing is a tough, dreary way to allay hunger. Robbing banks is hard, dangerous, dirty work. Raping women is completely unnecessary, even for the most lonely, homely, hungry individual. Why do things the hard way? What's wrong with a man's judgment, what is wrong with his education, when he does such things?

Psychiatrists do not say "sick." That is your word, not ours. We speak of pathological behavior. There is a difference. It may be socio-pathological; it may be psycho-pathological; all these big words merely mean that it can be treated, that something scientific can be done about it. That isn't what sick means. Sick means that the public takes a certain attitude toward it.

Psychiatrists deal all the time with people who act pathologically. In our offices people do peculiar things in peculiar ways. Often they don't know why they do them or how to stop doing them. Most of our patients haven't robbed any banks, but some of them have committed crimes. They usually haven't killed anybody. Most of them, like the rest of us, have thought about it. Most of our patients, like most of my friends, have done wilder things than write checks with insufficient funds.

What can we do about the situation? We could do just what the New York State Crime Commission recommended in 1927, which is the same thing Sheldon Glueck advocated in 1936, and which Felix Frankfurter proposed in 1959. In Justice Frankfurter's words: "I myself think that . . . judges are not very competent, are not qualified by experience to impose sentences where any discretion is to be exercised. I do not think it is in the domain of the training of lawyers to know what to do with a fellow after you find out he is a thief. I do not think legal training gives you any special competence. I, myself, hope that one of these days, and before long, we will divide the functions of criminal justice. I think the lawyers are the people who are competent to ascertain whether or not a crime has been committed. The whole scheme of common law judicial machinery . . . is peculiarly fitted for that task. But all the questions that follow upon ascertainment of guilt, I think require very different and much more diversified talents than the lawyers and judges are normally likely to possess."

Time and time again judges, and some doctors, have agreed that psychiatrists should forsake the courtroom and play a much larger role in the rehabilitation of offenders. If a man is really guilty of behaving badly, let us know; give us an opportunity to find out what was behind his kind of behavior.

There is a happy ending to this presentation. How many of you know that we Kansans have a Diagnostic Center to advise judges what to do after they find out that a man is guilty of a crime? The Center makes studies of the offender, of the kind of person he is, the kind of environment he has lived in, the kind of potentialities he has, and the best way he should be handled.

There has been one hair in the butter, however. After the Center has studied a man for two months, after a recommendation is made to the judge for either inpatient or outpatient treatment, as we doctors call it, whether he could be in an honor camp or go right back where he was and continue on parole, we have had no adequate place to take care of him and give him treatment. This is especially true of young people, who instead of going to the University of Kansas, enrolled in the "University of Rough Stuff." For a long time we have needed a treatment center where offenders could be taught rather than jailed. They need teaching but we haven't had a place or a way to do it. But the last legislature supplemented the Diagnostic Center with a Rehabilitation Center.

This new Rehabilitation Center will be one of the great additions to the educational facilities of our state. The people whom I have called offenders are citizens just as you are; they are citizens with whom you interact and whose paths will cross with yours. I want, and I know you want, to be surrounded with the best people possible, and if they are people below our standard I want to see them raised as high as possible. Many of them could go far higher than they have. Our rehabilitation center won't be the very first one in the United States, but I am proud of the fact that here Kansas has something that most other states haven't yet gotten around to: a Diagnostic Center—and now a Rehabilitation Center.

Remember, I am referring to human beings who are really our brothers and sisters as well as fellow citizens. Most of us who have had more fortunate lives can scarcely imagine the circumstances which have led these people in the wrong directions. I hear many of their stories. I hear many of the stories of patients in the state hospitals. I hear the stories of many private patients who have not been in any prison and who have not been in any state hospital but might very well have been in both. I know the stories of some university students. They all have something in common. They all share the vicissitudes of interaction between the individual and his environment, each striving to take advantage of opportunities that come his way and create new opportunities for himself. Some of these opportunities, good fortune gives him; others, bad fortune takes from him.

Some of what has been done to people can be undone. Most of it can. Most of it can be atoned for or made restitution for. Some of it cannot; some actions are tragically irrevocable. But in most instances our fellow citizens who commit crimes are potentially restorable by education of the right sort to constructive citizenship. In the meantime it is their God-given desert that we, their brethren, not commit further crimes against them but rather that we employ the scientific knowledge which has increased so vastly in recent years toward the salvage, the rehabilitation, the redirection, and the preservation of these fellow Kansans.

We can do it. We are about to do it. We have begun to do it. Let's not be weary in well doing; having put our hand to the plow let's turn the furrow like our brave and inspired forebears who planted the seeds of this great university. Their successors built our great state hospital program. They built our great state educational system, and we now approach a modern program for the re-education of offenders with a view to the greater safety, protection, and satisfaction of our citizens—you yourselves, and your children. All power and blessing to you, and to us all.

COMMENTARIES

MONTAGU: As an old student of crime I, like many of my colleagues, have come to the conclusion that crime is not really restricted to the state of Kansas, that it is found, of course, in every society where human beings are deprived of the opportunities for fulfilling themselves in a reasonably healthy environment, in relation to whatever that society holds out for them as success. It is complete rubbish for anyone, as Dr. Menninger pointed out, to speak of a born criminal or the criminal mind, to say that the criminal is incurable. It is non-sense to speak of criminal genes. Genes don't make criminals; what makes criminals is society. And society having made the criminals then punishes them for what they have caused them to become. As Dr. Menninger pointed out so eloquently, we believe that if anyone does commit a crime—a crime is being defined as whatever any society chooses at a particular time to call a crime—then the way to deal with him is to commit a crime against him, and thus having put two wrongs into the record that somehow makes it right.

The barbarous monstrosity is capital punishment. Not only does capital punishment not act as a deterrent, but actually provides a social sanction for the citizenry to go ahead and do likewise. Because if the state can commit such an offense, to take the life of another, why can't the individual? When we consider what lawyers have to say on this subject, I recall a view of what lawyers know in the form of an English poem:

> The law that lawyers know about
> Is property and land;
> But why the leaves are on the trees,
> And why the waves disturb the seas,
> Why honey is the food of bees,
> Why horses have such tender knees,
> Why winters come when rivers freeze,
> Why Faith is more than what one sees,
> And Hope survives the worst disease,
> And Charity is more than these,
> They do not understand.

I would take the administration of the law entirely out of the hands of the lawyers and put it where it belongs—in the hands of human beings like Dr. Menninger.

LARSON: I am bound to remind you that this verse was written about British lawyers. I was greatly indebted to Dr. Menninger for his repeated thoughtfulness in pointing out that in this ongoing struggle for modernization of the criminal system it is the psychiatrists and the forward-looking lawyers who have taken such a beating in the last couple of days—the status quo.

Dr. Menninger pointed out to me, following my observations on the need to apply something resembling the scientific method to international and other human affairs, that it wouldn't hurt me to take a look at the application of the same technique to the criminal law system. I thought I was involved in every controversy in the United States and many outside, but here is one I have seemed to have missed, and I will try to do something to make it right. In the meantime I am glad that the correct side is in the hands of such a competent champion as Dr. Menninger.

Dr. Menninger, who was on the panel last night, following
my opening remarks said that the best thing he could do in
relation to my presentation was to ask me a question rather than
to make a comment or criticism. And I am going to repay the
compliment this afternoon. Certainly I don't feel competent
to comment, much less to criticize, but I would like to ask a
question. This is not a kind of mutual arrangement between
us that we worked out in order to get through some of those
pages that he flipped over. This is sort of a follow-up to one
of the most fascinating avenues that he opened up to our view
that he wasn't able to elaborate on, so I would just like to ask
him this forthright question. I'll preface this by saying that
you drew a parallel between the mentally ill and the so-called
criminal offenders. You mentioned that about 90 per cent
leave mental hospitals with proper treatment within a short time.
Is it possible to say, within any reasonable bounds, what
proportion of people in penal institutions, or for that matter
under death sentences, could be rehabilitated given the
availability of optimum resources, including the new Diagnostic
Center, the new Rehabilitation Center? And perhaps could
you give us a little more on what would be the dimension of the
optimum institutional system that could bring about the greatest
rehabilitation of the greatest number?

MENNINGER: You know we don't know; you ask me
just to guess. In the first place, you said what number, who
are in the institution? Just as the new mental health center
endeavors to keep as many people as possible out of the state
hospital, even though they know the state hospital will do the
job if you have to go there, and get you out rather quickly,
I would think our aim would be to spare the state the expense
and the individual the consequences of jail sentences if possible.
Many judges feel this way, do they not, and try to do it? But
it is hard for an individual judge to depart from the customs of
the larger community. Judges have been cautious. Naturally.
The number of parole officers available has been small. We
have some honor camps in this state which have been successful.
Dr. Wescoe and I recommended them when we were on the
commission. They are working very well, but there are not
enough of them and not enough people to work with them.

We must keep remembering that we got a bad system started.
We have a whole lot of repeaters who are expert at this to keep
the bad stream going, and I think it would take time to correct.
But I think the time will come when the majority will be
affected in a positive way and treated in a different way. I don't
get up and say, "Jails must go!" There are a few people we have
ruined, they have ruined, their parents have ruined—somebody
ruined them—that we have to keep locked up. I don't think
anybody doubts that, but I certainly think the kind of jails we
have now should begin to diminish very rapidly in number
and content and everything else.

EISELEY: I think there are two things we should keep in
mind in connection with this problem. One involves the protection of society. The other involves the protection and
rehabilitation of the criminal. And these two things have been
confused at times and are somewhat at loggerheads now.

Let me give you an illustration. In my home town, as is
true of all great metropolitan areas, there are many violent
crimes committed almost every day. As one reads about the
individuals apprehended in this connection one frequently finds
that some are persons who have records as long as my arm.
For reasons unknown to the general public, they seem to be
out walking around, frequently during the time when they are
supposed to be at least under consideration as possible criminals
in other cases. I won't harass you with an account of individual
cases, many of them involving extremely atrocious crimes.
I have, however, been struck by the fact that criminals who have
demonstrated over a long period of years that, whatever their
innocent origins, they are now a menace on the streets of the
city, are out and walking about. I suspect that one of the
reasons is that the legal system is so antiquated that in one way
or another these offenders have run through a string of petty
sentences even though it might have been obvious, if they had
come under the attention of able psychiatrists, that they should
not be out on the street at all, irrespective of the crime which
brought them under observation. This leads to a consideration
of how people are to be sentenced and analyzed from this
standpoint. In one particular murder about which I happen to
know, the individual perpetrating this senseless killing had been

confined in a mental institution in the city. It turned out he
had not been legally released from the institution at all, but
had been, as they euphemistically phrased it, "missing for five
or six months." Why was he missing? Why had there been
so little effort to apprehend him? It was because the particular
institution in which he had been placed was so overcrowded that
the individuals involved in its management breathed a sigh of
relief every time somebody quietly walked out the back door
and disappeared. It meant that there was room for an incoming
person to be processed.

This is certainly not effective psychiatric handling, as Dr.
Menninger would agree. But it is the kind of curious, furtive
way in which handling of the mentally ill goes on in many of
our great metropolitan centers and elsewhere in the country.
I would venture to say that if we are to have justice without
malice, a justice tempered with compassion, we must have
some way other than these feeble little court sentences, which
are frequently meaningless and which vary enormously for the
same crime from state to state in the Union. We must in some
fashion make sure that dangerous individuals are kept out of
circulation, and this should be done in a rational, therapeutic
fashion, very carefully controlled.

There is the other question of the protection of society
as well as the protection of the criminal who is psychiatrically
disturbed. Here again we should give serious attention, as is
being given in a very few states, to the care and treatment of
those who have been violently wronged by atrocious assault, and
who are left broken in health, if they survive. In many instances
there seems to be more concern about the rehabilitation of the
criminal than about the innocent individual whose body may
have been permanently damaged by some dreadful experience
of this kind. I know of one person who no longer can speak,
whose mental powers are terribly injured, who by accident
survived a shooting with intent to kill. I do not know how that
individual will be cared for except through the help of friends,
or whatever paltry insurance he may have had. As we strive
toward the humanitarian goal which Dr. Menninger has so ably
propounded and spent his life upon, let me reiterate that we
must keep in mind the problem of the protection of the public,
of society, and of the injured individual, as well as the problem

of the protection and rehabilitation of the criminal. In these areas I think our laws are patently inadequate and should be reexamined and further analyzed in the light of knowledge now available to us.

MONTAGU: As a parting shot, let me say that I agree with what Dr. Menninger says. All investigators have agreed that the criminal, so-called, must be treated as if he were mentally ill and that the jail is not the proper place in which to perform such treatment. Since Dr. Menninger has spoken of the public apathy in this matter, I would like to drop a bomb. I was called in as a physical anthropologist to examine the bones and teeth of a nine-year-old girl who had been murdered by a man who was seventy-two years of age. He was apprehended two years after I had examined the body. When he was interrogated—and this is in the public record—he confessed to having committed many other murders in the course of his life. You may read this story in Wertham's book *The Show of Violence.* As Wertham said when he emerged from the cell where he had examined the old man for the first time, this man suffered from more mental disorders than any textbook has yet described. He had been released from Bellevue in New York two weeks before he committed this last murder. The police investigated thirteen of his confessed crimes and stopped at that number having decided that this constituted sufficient verification of the others he had claimed. He had been in Bellevue Hospital for eighteen months and was dismissed. The police and others went back to Bellevue and asked, "Why did you dismiss him?" "Well," they said, "what could we do? We are a public hospital, we are a city hospital, we are overloaded— he was occupying a bed, and he seemed a nice, innocent old man to us."

This is the way we handle this kind of situation in our society. Until the public loses some of its apathy and involves itself more deeply in its fellow man's welfare, particularly those we so wrongly call criminals, we shall go on committing the kind of errors and follies and crimes that are being discussed here.

MENNINGER: I am very grateful to my three kind critics. Now a word if I may to each of them. I would not like to have this meeting close with the idea that most terrible crimes are committed by some crazy man that the psychiatrist has let slip. There are a lot of crazy men that we psychiatrists never see. Some of us have times, you know, when we do somewhat peculiar things. To determine a pattern of a man's life behavior is not an easy trick. Sometimes some psychiatrists who have the opportunity to do it do make mistakes. But though one, two, three, or a hundred may escape, I wish you would be grateful to the psychiatrists of this state, and every state, who have taken care of hundreds of people like that who don't get out and hurt you and who are under supervision.

It bothers us to have one of our mistakes going around and to hear people say, "Just look. You let that fellow go." Yes, somebody let go the boys who killed the Clutter family. Sounds to me by reading the account that it shouldn't have been done, but that is making the diagnosis by aftersight. I wasn't there. You must remember that they may not have had the legal authority to detain those boys anymore. I haven't looked it up, but it is very possible that they didn't have. Mr. McAtee is doing a fine job and Mr. Noble, in charge of the place in Topeka, is an excellent man; Hutchinson is improving and Lansing has a good warden. We are doing better, but these men are limited by what they are told by the judge. "You may keep this man seven years minus good time." He doesn't have the right to find this man a dangerous character. Then you have to prove that he is a dangerous character, and that is not an easy thing to do. You can prove most any of us are dangerous characters if you put us in a box with some bumblebees. It depends on the circumstances.

To make predictions and to play God is something I urge my psychiatric students not to do. Describe what you see and let predictions be for somebody else. If the person seems dangerous then the judicial authorities may detain him.

I am a little surprised that Dr. Eiseley should remind me that we should consider the safety of the public. It is because of the safety of the public we should stop committing crimes against criminals. The revolving-door business of having offenders go in and out—stop and think about it! According to the St. Louis Crime Survey, of a thousand people who commit crimes only one hundred are ever detected and caught.

Of the one hundred caught only about ten are found guilty and sentenced. Of the ten, only one serves his sentence. It is a little different now, but not much. If every one of you had committed a crime last week only three or four of you would serve a sentence. I am talking about these three or four who become professional criminals, whose lives are ruined. Often they could be saved. The protection of the public doesn't mean we have to catch half a dozen bad boys and lock them up. We musn't do that. Crime doesn't stem from just half a dozen bad boys; you know that. Crime stems from all of us.

Which is the more serious crime, to drive ninety-five miles an hour on the turnpike or to forge a check? What threatens the safety of society most, I ask you? Stop and think of the crimes that you and I are near to doing. Of course society must be protected and that is what we must base our actions on; this does not mean that everybody with the slightest likelihood of harming society must be locked up. I know the lawyers won't be a party to that and I think we psychiatrists would be with them. We'd say, "Look, you can't lock up the whole country—because all of us have aggressive impulses." All of us under some circumstances could do violent things. The question is—which people seem to have established a pattern to do so and which of these people can we help to change this pattern. That was what I was speaking for. Next time I get to make a speech I'll talk to you about the other end of the thing, which is the whole problem of policing. And that begins by saying that we should double or triple the police force, double or triple their salaries, double or triple the qualifications for policemen. Then you would have some protection. That's another time.

MAN AND THE FUTURE | 8

EXPLORATIONS IN TOMORROW

Arthur C. Clarke

I intend to talk about three aspects of the future. This talk will be in three episodes or fits. One will concern the exploration of space; the second, the exploration of the sea; and the third, a field which may be more important than either.

Contrary to anything that may have been said, it is not possible to predict the future. All one can do is outline various possibilities and then wait to see what happens. In a book I wrote some years ago called *Profiles of the Future*, I evolved something which I then called Clarke's Law. It ran as follows: "If a distinguished but elderly scientist says that something is possible he is almost certainly correct. If he says that something is impossible he is very probably wrong." By elderly scientist I meant anyone over thirty.

Since then Clarke's Second Law emerged in a French review of that book. I hadn't thought of a second law, but another one was pointed out. I had said, "The only way one can find the limits of the possible are by going beyond them into the impossible." Of course, this is only a variation on the old remark which I think is by Max Beerbohm but sounds like Oscar Wilde, "The art of living is knowing where to stop and going a little further."

Even later I derived Clarke's Third Law which is possibly the most important, "Any advanced technology is indistinguishable from magic." I'd like you to think about that. I'd like you to ask yourself what Edison would have thought of solid-state electronics. And that isn't going so very far back. We have quantum jumps in technology, and with each quantum jump the technology of the next era is magic to that of the preceding era. So if you bear these three laws in mind I hope I have softened you up for some of the more outrageous things I shall be saying later.

The first frontier I want to talk about is space. Confidentially I'm getting a little bored with space, possibly because I've been writing about it for thirty years. It's such an obvious frontier now that almost anything one can say about space is a cliché. Nevertheless, the important thing about clichés is that they're true. A lot of people, even now, don't realize this. As many of you know, there was a recent poll in *Science*—I'm terribly sorry that Dr. Abelson isn't here because I've been saving this all the way round from Ceylon—about the space program which was mailed out to about three thousand scientists. About half of them replied, and the majority were against it, at least in regard to the Apollo program, as being a waste of money, a diversion of money that could be used effectively elsewhere.

This is a perfectly legitimate viewpoint and I have some sympathy for it. You can argue that our billions are being wasted on space. But you can't help wasting money on an enormous program like this. Where I violently disagree with this poll was that no less than 4 per cent of the scientists questioned said that there was no scientific value in landing a man on the moon. Now any scientist who can say that there is no scientific value in landing a man on the moon is a moron. To prevent any misunderstanding, I should say that if you had a poll among British scientists the percentage might be a little higher.

Anyway, this attitude, the belief that manned space flight is a waste of money, will seem so inconceivable in another decade that we'll forget that it ever happened, just as we forget that sixty years ago distinguished scientists were saying that men would never be able to fly. The best example of that is the great astronomer, Simon Newcomb, who wrote a classic paper on the impossibility of manned flight which is still well worth reading: it will convince you; it will make you take the train the next time you have to go anywhere. The paper was published just before the Wrights flew. Incidentally, it still isn't generally realized in the United States that when the Wrights flew in 1903 it was about three years before the newspapers got around to reporting that fact, and people didn't realize that the conquest of air had occurred until several years later. When it was pointed out to Newcomb that man had flown despite his paper he had his reply ready. He said, "Ah, yes, they may build an airplane to carry a man but never a passenger as well."

I want to say a few words about the exploration of our first target in space, the moon. Why is the moon of such overwhelming scientific importance? For this reason: until now we have had only one sample of a planet to study and I am sure you all realize that one sample is very poor statistics. There's hardly a field of science which will not be revolutionized when you have two samples.

One obvious field is astronomy. The moon might have been designed as a base for astronomical observatories. It has perfect visibility, never has any bad weather; it has no weather at all. It has a low gravity so you can build very large structures. One of the advantages of no weather, which people tend to overlook, is the absence of wind, which is extremely important for radio observatories. In fact, the ideal place for a radio observatory is undoubtedly the far side of the moon because there you are shielded from all the electronic racket of the earth, permanently shielded by two thousand miles of solid rock. I haven't worked this out, but I think it is possible that the lunar far side may now be the only quiet place in the solar system. So the really big radio observatories of the future will be there. (I might mention that the really, really big radio observatories will probably be in space itself.) You may be fascinated to know, and this is right up Mr. Fuller's street, that there are now designs being studied for radio telescopes up to seventy miles in diameter. And the fascinating thing is that they weigh only about a hundred pounds and can be launched by existing rockets. They are simply spinning webs which will expand by centrifugal force.

The moon is also the ideal testing place for the techniques of further exploration. We can carry out our first steps into space only two days away so that if we make mistakes at least there's a chance of a little help from the home office. Another important thing we have to do on the moon is to learn to turn rocks into food. We haven't been clever enough yet to do what every plant does, but we've got to learn fairly quickly. I think some of these techniques are going to be developed very quickly. There already are contracts with the Air Force for processing lunar rocks and turning them into food. It will have great repercussions here on earth.

I might mention the subject of transportation. Of course you can't have airplanes on the moon and ballistic transport, I think, is always going to be rather expensive—being fired in a rocket, taking off at high G, coasting, and landing. You're under several Gs for some of the flight and zero G for most of it. In fact I've defined ballistic transportation as transportation in which half the time the toilet is out of reach and half the time it's out of order. So on the moon we'll probably have to have surface transportation again. And—I think this is a poignant thought—contrary to what is generally considered, the great age of railroads was not the nineteenth century, it will be the twenty-first century on the moon. Because there in vacuum conditions and lower gravity, you can build railroads—there are some stability problems, I know, but there are also solutions—that can operate at a thousand miles an hour. This is one of the ways we'll have to get around between the different lunar cities.

There's been a great deal of debate as to what the surface of the moon is like, whether it is covered with dust. I wrote a novel on the idea that there are pools of dust, although I was very careful to say there weren't very many of them, and I put the one I used in my story in a very out-of-the-way place so that it will take at least twenty years to prove it isn't there.

The day after Lunar 9 landed on the moon and photographs came back I had a phone call from the public relations department of the Kremlin. A charming young lady, who caught me in London after pursuing me from Colombo, said that because my books were so popular in the Soviet Union what comments did I have on Lunar 9? It was with great difficulty that I refrained from answering that if they were so popular what about some rubles?

Another enormously important use of the moon is going to be as a base, a jumping-off spot for further explorations, because the energy you need to get away from a celestial body is proportional to its gravitational field and its radius, to G times R. And as the moon has only a sixth of the earth's gravity and a quarter of the radius, it's about twenty-five times easier to get off the moon, to escape from the moon, in terms of energy, as it is from the earth. Which means that the moon, although it's only a quarter of a million miles away, is 95 per cent of the way to the planets, because in space travel it's energy that counts. Distance is meaningless, immaterial.

In the colonization of the moon, which will be one of the major projects of the closing decades of this century and in the next century, we will meet again the kind of pioneering spirit which we have seen in the past, which is part of your history. And this is why I get so annoyed with people who say we can explore the moon by automatic devices. This misses the whole point. We could have stayed in Europe and explored America by automatic devices. The point is that one day we'll be living in these places. This, of course, is a tremendous challenge. The technology of planetary engineering is still only a dream of the future; but we know, just as we moved into places that were once totally uninhabitable on this earth, we shall do the same thing to these new lands in the sky. Ask yourself what the pioneers in covered wagons would have thought as they struggled through the Arizona desert. They would not have thought that one day there would be gracious living in the places where they were leaving their bones and their wagon wheels.

As a matter of fact, the argument that we can do everything by automatic devices, that we don't need men in space, has been refuted on several levels. Last week this country launched perhaps its most important satellite, the orbiting astronomical observatory on which about fifty million dollars had been spent. It's useless, it failed, we don't know why. It might have been fixed by a man with a screw driver. We have to have man in space to service, to replenish, to repair the dozens of different types of vehicles—space probes, orbiting satellites, orbiting observatories—which we are launching. People often say that it's ridiculous to talk about space colonization because it takes, I think, about a thousand dollars at the moment to put one pound into orbit. Well, I don't know what the economics of the first airplanes were, but I merely mention one fact of energy—and energy is what matters to you in space—to show what the potentialities are. The energy released by a single large thermonuclear bomb, which isn't a very big device, is sufficient to send the United States Navy to Mars and to bring it back to earth. Now at the moment we can only use a fraction of that energy for propulsion, but the energy is there; we have released it.

Potentially space travel need be no more expensive than aviation. But we know practically nothing about the other planets. (We shall learn a lot more with our forthcoming space probes.) All we know is that the surface area of at least two hundred earths is scattered around the solar system. There is enough scientific knowledge to occupy man for centuries. Of course Mars is still the most fascinating target. It's amusing to see how the debate rages on the subject of life on Mars. I suppose when the first Mariner photographs came in there was a feeling of disappointment—there were no princesses or anything like that. But as Carl Sagan and others have pointed out, the search for life on earth at the same resolution gives no proof at all that this planet is inhabited. Since then even the canal controversy is still going strong because, contrary to the first reports, there is one canal very clearly visible on the Mariner II photograph, although it's far too small for Lowell to have seen. It's an absolutely linear feature, apparently a crack running right across the photograph. I'm sure we'll have permanent bases, perhaps ultimately very large colonies, on Mars in the next century.

I don't know what we're going to do about the giant planets. They're quite a challenge. These enormous worlds are as unimaginable to us as the oceans would be to desert dwellers. They're very cold and enormous. Take Jupiter, for example. It means little to say that it's eleven times the diameter of earth, but a mental picture I have does give me some feeling for the size of Jupiter. If you took the earth and skinned it and pinned that skin on the face of Jupiter, it would look about the same size as India looks on the earth. There's an awful lot of territory on Jupiter. We're not even sure if we can ever approach it, but it'll have to be in something like a bathyscaphe as well as a space ship.

The problem which fascinates everybody is: are there any other life forms on the planets or in space? Well, the solar system looks very unpromising as of now, but I think we should still be prepared for surprises. It's little more than a hundred years ago that scientists were completely confident that there could be no life at the bottom of the ocean. At a pressure of a thousand atmospheres, freezing temperatures, and total darkness, it's ridiculous to think of such a thing. Well, of course, the abyss is full of life. Life seems to move into every possible place. With some difficulty I can imagine life forms that could exist on any one of the planets. It's true I can't imagine them getting started on some of the planets as they are today, because it's hard to imagine life ever originating except in an aqueous environment, but once it has started it can do some very remarkable things. And we may have some surprises when we land on Mars, possibly even unpleasant surprises. Or perhaps it's the Martians who'll have the most unpleasant surprises.

It does seem, however, that we've got to look farther afield for life, certainly for intelligent life. And here has been a tremendous revolution in outlook in the last two decades. I can remember the books of Jeans and Eddington in the thirties and even later when the attitude was that the planets were freaks; we might be the only planetary system in the universe. This situation has changed completely and now it's believed that planetary systems are very common—that possibly most stars, certainly a very high percentage of them, have planets. Where you go from here depends on your optimism; anything is a "guesstimate." If you're an optimist you may say that given planets life will fill them all automatically, and intelligence may then follow also almost automatically in almost every case. If you're a pessimist you may say, well, it may happen only once in a million times. Dr. Shapley in his book on stars and men has gone into this.

Here is another statistic I would like to throw at you. The total number of suns in our island universe is rather more than a hundred thousand million. Now that again is a figure that doesn't mean anything, but perhaps it may mean something now. That is roughly the total of all the men who have ever lived since the beginning of time. So for every man that has ever lived there is one sun in our galaxy alone. If there were only one sun in a thousand with life around it that would be a hundred million inhabited systems.

Can they ever be contacted across the light years? Well, there's a great debate going on about this, a debate between transportation and communication. The engineering problem of interstellar travel is quite trivial. It's not generally known that a Saturn 5 could send a Volkswagen to Alpha Centauri. There's only one slight snag—it would take a quarter million years to get there. So, as it's been pointed out, the problem of intersolar flight is not an engineering problem; it's a biological problem. However, there are several ways in which one could imagine, if one is rather optimistic, that even physical intersolar flight might be possible—perhaps on a multi-generation basis in a space ship which is really a little world, self-contained. After all we're on a space ship right now heading roughly toward Vega. When we get there, of course, Vega will be somewhere else. We might make smaller vehicles that are controllable and move much faster. J. B. S. Haldane once remarked to me that he thought the human race might have been adapted for interstellar flight because at our natural acceleration you reach the nearest stars in a year or so, which is a reasonable length of time. But here again the problem is that there are no power sources known which could provide a sustained acceleration of one G and, of course, a deceleration of one G the second half of the journey. Nevertheless, I don't think we should rule out this possibility. For example, the recent discovery of the quasars which are now convulsing the astronomical fraternity at least suggests that there are energy sources much more powerful even than nuclear energy.

If physical interstellar flight is possible, it's certainly possible by automatic space probes. It may take thousands of years; but if it's possible for living creatures then, of course, we come to the problem of where is everybody? Why hasn't somebody come here? I refuse to discuss flying saucers, partly because I shall be doing it on "CBS Reports" shortly, and partly for a very simple reason. If you've never seen any flying saucers you're not very observant, and if you've seen as many as I have you won't believe in them.

Seriously—and this is a serious subject that has received little serious attention—I think we should keep our eyes open for historical or archeological evidence for visits in the past because in the millions of years that lie behind us it seems to me very possible that there may have been expeditions here; this, in fact, is the theme of the Kubrick-Clarke movie, 2001: A Space Odyssey. I keep an eye open for odd and inexplicable phenomena. What I'm following at the moment is the discovery in the last decade in a Chinese tomb dated, I think, about the second century A.D.—this is written up in one of the Chinese historical journals—of some clothing; there is nothing unusual about this, but among the clothing was a very badly corroded buckle and that buckle was 75 per cent aluminum. Now this is a shocking thing to anyone who knows anything about metallurgy. We've got Dr. Joseph Needham on the job at the moment and I hope to find that this has been either a mistake or a hoax. If it's not we're in trouble. There's no way of making aluminum without an advanced electro-technology.

Even if interstellar transportation is impossible we are fairly sure that communication is feasible and it would almost certainly be very much cheaper. Even with present technologies, with our present antenna systems, such as the thousand-foot-diameter radio-telescope in Puerto Rico, we could send signals about a hundred light years and receive them over the same distance with the same transmitter power. And if we can do this fifty years after having discovered radio, then any advanced civilization could do very much better. Hence the efforts that have been made on a very small scale, which I hope will be repeated on a larger scale, to listen for intelligent signals from space. It's a very difficult technical problem: where do you listen, what frequency, where do you point your antenna? It's much worse than looking for a station on the short wave dial. You don't know where it is because you have the odd sort of problem of directivity as well as frequency. One problem, as has been pointed out, is that because it's cheaper to listen than to transmit everybody may be listening.

I'd like to end this section on space by mentioning the rarified speculations of the Russian astronomer, Joseph Shovsky, who's one of the leading astrophysicists in the U.S.S.R. and has been very much concerned with this idea. He has suggested that civilizations may be grouped in three categories. A Type One civilization is our type which has at its disposal rather trivial energy resources. I forget how many horsepower we have but about ten to the twelfth horsepower, something on that order. A Type Two civilization is one which has harnessed the entire energy output of its star. And a Type Three civilization is one which has harnessed the entire energy output of its galaxy. And he suggests that instead of trying to listen for signals from the other stars in our galaxy we should look to Andromeda because there we have a whole system of a hundred thousand million suns in a rather small area, a few degrees across. And one Type Two beacon would be easily visible across that two million light years. We should look for unusual astronomical phenomena which don't seem explicable in terms of natural forces. Freeman Dyson of the Institute of Advanced Studies has suggested along similar lines that an advanced civilization would trap all the energy of its sun, not waste all that power. Of course, the power would eventually radiate but degraded into the infrared so we should look out for infrared sources of considerable angular diameter. And these may be advanced civilizations, and what we will be picking up will be the waste heat of the really advanced civilizations.

There are all sorts of other possibilities, but now I want to come back from the remote depths of space and switch to inner space, the oceans which cover two-thirds of this earth.

In the seas we are still primitive hunters; we're still in the Stone Age. It's time that agriculture, or aquaculture if you like, was developed to harness the gigantic resources of the ocean, which is far more productive than the land. I have suggested that whale ranching might be an interesting possibility in the next century. The whale is the world's largest cattle: it weighs fifty tons or more and produces excellent milk, much better quality than cows give. If they're intelligent, of course, we could herd them. But

I'm afraid, since I wrote the book that I called *The Deep Range*, it looks as if there may be no whales by the year 2000 because they're being slaughtered ruthlessly. It is an example of genocide which hasn't received the attention it should. All the whaling fleets have been over-fishing—that's the wrong word—over-hunting whales, and the situation got so bad that all other countries dropped out of the whaling business and sold their fleets to the Japanese who are just trying to slaughter to get enough money to repay their capital expenditure, and to heck with the next generation. There'll be no whales left unless something is done about this. This also raises a moral problem because we know that whales are intelligent; after all they're large dolphins and we all know about dolphins. They may even be more intelligent than we are. (Actually I have doubts about the intelligence of the dolphin because it seems too friendly to man.) But perhaps we're unjustified in hunting or hurting whales, because even if they're not very bright they may have a much higher morality than we have on some scale of ethics upon which perhaps intelligent extraterrestrials might rate creatures.

Another possibility is sea farms. I think that it is ridiculous farming our land. In the sea you have no irrigation problem. One problem you do have is that much of the sea in the tropics is infertile because the nutrients are trapped; they have fallen to the bottom of the abyss, particularly the phosphates which ultimately determine the productivity of the oceans. About ten years ago I suggested that we might be able to produce artificial upwelling of these nutrient chemicals by submerging nuclear reactors, and the heat of the reactors would start deep sea fountains and bring this material up to the top and in fact fertilize the sea. It would result in a tremendous increase in plankton growth, and the fish feast on the plankton, and so forth. If we do develop plankton farms, of course, we will have the problem of harvesting this material and processing it. It may be rather difficult to harvest plankton. We'd have to design a kind of mobile processing plant, and by the time we've done this engineering feat we may find the whale does it better anyway. So we might as well go back to the whales and let them feed on our farms and then slaughter them.

Apart from the food productivity side of the sea, the mineral wealth of the oceans is almost inexhaustible and almost untapped. We are betting bromine and magnesium and, of course, salt from the sea. From the sea we are starting to get the most important chemical of all, water. There are vast deposits on the ocean bed, all sorts of metals, in particular manganese, which are still untouched; there's a huge technology waiting there.

Changing the subject only slightly, the sea is the greatest untouched museum. I've seen estimates that about a fifth of the wealth of mankind lies at the bottom of the sea. Our history is there waiting to be discovered. The reason, of course, is that the great trade routes of the world are over the sea and the sea has been exacting tribute ever since man built ships. Underwater archeology is just beginning. It's a fascinating subject. I got involved in it in Ceylon. We found a ship, quite a recent one, 1702, containing about a ton of silver, lying ten miles off the coast. And we've been working on that for several years. The treasure it carried is still in sacks of coins weighing thirty pounds each. I gave one to the Smithsonian where it's on display in Washington, tax deductible, of course.

But more interesting than mere money are things like the ancient Greek computer found in a wreck of Antikythera in 1900. You may have seen the story on this in *Scientific American* about 1959. Here was an advanced analogue computer dated 100 B.C. No one even dreamed that the Greeks could make such complex devices. It's an astronomical computer which is roughly equivalent to the kind of things we might have built five hundred years ago in the West. In Athens last summer I got them to show it to me, and this mass of corroded gear wheels gave me an extraordinary feeling that I was looking at a technology which was not two thousand years old. And I thought, if that culture had continued in a linear way—well, by this time we would have been at Rigel, because that thing was only five hundred years from the space ship in linear development. Nobody knows where it came from or who built it.

At the moment people like Jacques Cousteau and, of course, Ed Link of the U.S. Navy are developing techniques for living on the bed of the ocean and working there. And when it comes along don't miss Cousteau's magnificent movie of his last work, *World Without Sun*, which is really the first space movie, because this type of underwater life is just like the kind of life we'd have on other planets. Here is a totally enclosed colony of men who have no connection at all, at least only a remote one, with life on the surface.

It is often thought there is some conflict between the money spent on space and the effort that goes into it and that spent on the sea. Some critics maintain that we should put more money into the sea. Well, there's no real conflict; the techniques of the two media are very similar. People interested in one are equally interested in the other. There's a feedback between them. I would say we certainly should put more money in the sea and we can afford to do so and it will pay off. I would say as purely an arbitrary judgment that for the near future the sea is much more important than space, but for the far future space will be more important than the sea.

After tantalizing your hope that some of these possibilities of discovery and exploration are real, most of it shall happen, I would like to end on a rather more somber note, changing the subject completely again, to the third type of exploration, the exploration of mind. But I'm not referring to human minds; I'm referring to ultra-intelligent machines. This is a subject which we are just beginning to consider, and it hasn't had the study yet that it deserves. I've got a paper which appeared in *Advances in Computers*; it's by Irving John Good, a fellow at Trinity College, Oxford. His opening sentence is: "The survival of man depends on the early construction of an ultra-intelligent machine. Let an ultra-intelligent machine be defined as a machine that can far surpass all the intellectual activities of any man, however clever. Since the design of machines is one of those intellectual activities, an ultra-intelligent machine could design even better machines. There would then unquestionably be an intelligence explosion and the intelligence of man would be left far behind. Thus the first ultra-intelligent machine is the last invention that man need ever make, providing that the machine is docile enough to tell him how to keep it under control."

Notice the wording: it doesn't say "provided the machine is docile enough to stay under control," but "docile enough to tell us how to keep it under control." (It is curious that this point is made so subtly on the other side of science fiction. It is sometimes worthwhile to take science fiction seriously.) This long and very complex paper and others of a similar type I could refer you to are concerned with how one would develop ultra-intelligent machines. Good believes we'll have them by the end of this century. In the not-very-seriously-intended time scale of mine which was quoted in various places, I said we wouldn't have them till the year 2080. It's often said you can't make ultra-intelligent machines; how can man build machines cleverer than man? This is nonsense; this is ridiculous. Well, the objection is ridiculous and I just can't imagine intelligent men making it. Once you make a machine which can learn —this has been done in principle in certain limited cases— there is no end to the process. Already there's a checker-playing machine which has not only succeeded in beating its maker but can beat all but about twelve people in the world and will soon be able to handle them.

There's an analogy which occurred to me while I was writing this paper, the machine tool analogy. If you told anyone in the Stone Age, an intelligent stone-ager chipping flints, that one day it would be possible to machine materials to an accuracy of a fraction of a millionth of an inch, he would say, "That's ridiculous. How can you possibly get to such a degree of precision chipping flints?" Tools improve tools, of course, and brains can improve brains without limit. Some of the consequences of this are rather shattering. One of them, which leads me back to my opening subject, is that possibly any advanced extra-terrestrials would be non-organic, which would of course make them highly suited for interstellar flight because machines don't mind waiting around for thousands of years. They don't mind vacuum conditions; in fact they probably prefer them. They don't mind high accelerations. So if we do have any visitors from space I suggest they won't come in space ships, they will be space ships.

Well, how does this affect us? Is this a pessimistic outlook? I don't know; it's part of the evolutionary process. Evolution had to pass through the organic phase. It's hard to see how on a lifeless planet an IBM computer could evolve without passing through the organic phase first, and maybe the next step in evolution is this sort of thing. Nietzsche once said that man is a rope stretched between the animal and the superhuman. Man is a bridge across the abyss. So perhaps when you have your next centennial, as I'm sure and hope you will, I wonder how many of the participants will be human. For that matter, how many of the audience.

COMMENTARIES

CONBOY: We have four distinguished genuine humans, I know, who would be happy to respond and one of the most human is Dr. Shapley.

SHAPLEY: I'm just a machine. I haven't been greased much lately. These colleagues of mine, I think, will answer questions and discuss the future with you. If you do not mind I would like to talk a little about the recent past, and then trust to my ingenious machines to take the subject further.

It has occurred to me in recent times that we, you, I, the scientists, and non-scientists, have revolutionized man's views about the world. So I made a list of the ten revelations that seem to have affected man's view of himself and the world in recent times. We won't go far enough back to get Darwinism or spectrum-analysis—no, but we'll go back to the first of this century. And I have here a list of ten enterprises, achievements that man has accomplished in that time, all of which have made his life different from what it would have been if we hadn't been so ingenious.

I'll just go through the list; it won't take long. The achievements are not in the proper order, they aren't in any kind of order. I just put down as number one, the origin of life. That is an enterprise on which we've done a great deal in the last few years. It's a chemical evolution.

Number two is cosmic evolution. That is, the evolution of everything. We know about the evolution of plants and animals and societies, governments, and things of that kind; and we have learned about the evolution of stars and of the velocities in the stars, and of galaxies. We now think we have pretty good evidence of the evolution of the atoms of matter themselves. The nickel, iron, and chromium atoms in this microphone are descendants from mother atom, hydrogen.

Number three, relativity, both special and general; it has changed our way of looking at space and time. It is indeed revolutionary.

Number four is galaxies and the expanding universe, one of which I've messed in a little bit. One of the greatest concepts of this century undoubtedly has been the expanding universe concept.

Number five, corpuscular sciences. By that I mean the sciences dealing with corpuscles of matter, the smallest things, and therefore X-rays would come into this; lasers would come into one particular group of the corpuscular sciences.

Number six, you'd all agree is sensational, Sputnikery. You know about Sputnikery.

Medical triumphs. You realize a quarter of you wouldn't be here if it hadn't been for what science has done in a medical sort of a way since the beginning of this century. I may have been exaggerating that a little but not much. It's just sensational, just to name the words, you know, of things that have come about, diseases and cures. Yes, the medicinal triumph is certainly one of my ten.

Number eight is cybernetics. We couldn't be without cybernetics and the computing machines; they are tremendously important. And they are changing our way of working at life. DNA and the genetic problems—I wouldn't want anybody to ask me about that because I don't understand it myself, and I'm not sure that my colleagues would, so we'll just say that number nine is DNA and number ten, exploration of the mind. I wrote that first "Freudian" exploration of the human mind; then I thought, this isn't all Freudian. There are minds in dogs and in all animals and amoeba, so I just left out the word "Freudian" and had it exploration of the human mind; then I left off "human," as too restrictive. So I have got it now; number ten is exploration of the mind.

Now I just say them over quickly, these ten seem to me pretty important in our grasping at our little chunk of eternity: origin of life, cosmic evolution, relativity theories, galaxies and expanding universes, corpuscular sciences, Sputnikery, medicinal triumphs, cybernetics and computing, and exploration of the mind. I think I've just done my share of pointing out what the recent past is and some of us can guess what some of the future's going to be, but already that has been done somewhat by you, sir, as to what the future's going to be. And number one I would put in that future the exploration of the ocean from top to bottom.

FULLER: I thought of many, many things as Dr. Clarke spoke but in this short time I shall only be able to comment on one or two. In relation to the immediate undertakings by world society of the answers to questions that have arisen today about spending money for the space program, I'd like to point out something that I find of interest. I have been concerned with the scientific development of controlled environments for men for the past forty years, and I learned very early that the great historical applications of science have been fundamentally underwritten by the munitions industries and the weapons programs of the great nations. When scientists designed the cannon, they didn't have to do anything about the man who fired the cannon. He could sleep beside the cannon and there was air for him to breathe; there was water near at hand; inclement temperature could be offset by clothing. Science produced bigger guns and floated them on battleships. Men, then, could sleep on the deck. However, now that scientific warfare has gone into space, men who handle the warfaring apparatus in space find no air to breathe and no water or food waiting to drink or eat. For the first time in history, it is of prime necessity for science to upgrade the environmental and metabolic regeneration conditions of man and to package them for economic delivery by rockets. To do so requires that science understands man as a process. When the astronauts go beyond the thermos bottle and sandwich excursion limits and must live for protracted periods on the moon or elsewhere in space, all the regenerative conditions provided by the biological interactions within the biosphere around the earth's surface will have to be reproduced in a miniaturized and capsulized human ecology which will emulate all the chemical and physical transactions necessary to sustain the process "man." All the apparatus to do so will be contained in a little black box weighing about five hundred pounds and measuring about twenty cubic feet. Man in space with the little black box will be able to regenerate his many organic processes and will need only small annual additions to the recirculating chemistry and physical transforming.

The first men living comfortably in space by virtue of the little black box will be watched by television cameras through every moment of their time and therefore be witnessed by continuously rotating audiences of two billion humans on earth. The whole of humanity will be swiftly educated on the uses and success of living with an entirely new sort of environmental control mechanics. To be successful, the new apparatus will have to operate as unconsciously, on the astronaut's part, as do all humans' internal organic processes when functioning correctly. Men are aware of their internal organisms only when they get a pain in the tummy, or of their eyes when they get a cinder in them.

The little five-hundred-pound black box will have to be produced on earth. The astronauts will not be asked to produce their own black box in space. Though the first black box will probably cost the United States and Russia combined over seven billion dollars, it should thereafter be reproducible on earth for about $2 a pound. This means that a one-thousand-dollar little black box could be rented profitably for no more than $200 per year. Any individual together with his family could take a black box, costing approximately $18 a month, and go to any remote, beautiful, dollar-a-year rental, or wilderness park land part of earth—mountain peak or desert island—and enjoy essential services superior to those now available in any city complex, because the sewers and energy lines will all be replaced and improved upon by the little autonomously recirculating black box.

The "black box" as domestic technology "fall-out" from the space and munitions programs will constitute the first wholesale application of science directly to making man a physical and economic success from anywhere in universe which, of course, includes "on earth." It will swiftly divert first-hand application of science from almost exclusive preoccupation with weapons development and their support and the latter's heretofore almost inexorable nose-dive towards self-extermination.

I would like now to change subjects very rapidly and go on to something else touched on by Arthur Clarke. I'll begin by asking if there is anything in our experience that can tell us if man might have an essential function to perform in universe. Is he needed in universe or is he—as he sometimes feels himself— just a chance observer, a theater-goer watching a great play called life? This is the kind of question posed by Shakespeare and I would like to explain the answer that I have found. The only way we can judge if man has a function or not is to go to our experimental data, and the way it works out is as follows:

All local systems of physical universe are entropic because, as experiments show, physical universe is always losing energies locally even though those same energies may be incorporated into other local systems. For example, the stars are sending off energies rapidly, but since the stars themselves are moving very rapidly with respect to one another, the energies radiated off are distributed very diffusely. Due to the continual intermotions and transformations of physical phenomena, energies released from local systems tend to become ever more diffused. As they bcome more and more diffused, they occupy more and more space. This is one of the observable characteristics of entropy. Expanding universe, as discussed by Dr. Shapley, is inherent in entropy. Then physical universe is entropic, expanding, increasingly diffuse, and, as the mathematicians would say, increasing in disorder or the random element.

This made me look for a kind of functioning in universe to balance this, since it is also part of our observations of the general scheme of physical universe that each fundamental patterning has a kind of complementary set of events. These complementary sets of events are not necessarily mirror images of each other. They succeed in balancing one another much as positive and negative balance one another. Therefore, I felt that there must be some phase of universe that is concurrently contracting and increasingly orderly to balance expanding, entropic physical universe. How could that be found? Astronomers, who had the same intuitive urge, looked into universe for black bodies that might be energy inhibiting, but the kinds of telescopes that, until only very recently, were available, were not suitable for finding non-radiant black bodies.

I saw that around our own little spaceship earth exist high and low atmospheric "pressures," which might better be called expanding and contracting atmospheric patterns. I discovered clues to the operation of a contracting universe to be operative on our own planet. For example, the planet earth is not radiant: if it were, we could not live on it. Earth is not sending off energy to any important degree. Compared to a star, it is "dead." Earth is receiving energy from the sun, but not losing it at the same rate. In addition to its daily sun radiation income, earth receives a continually increasing inventory of radiation in its lethal, sifting, sorting, and accumulating Van Allen belts. A succession of concentric terrestrial spheres such as the ionosphere, troposphere, etc., constitutes an extraordinary series of random-to-orderly sorting, shunting, partially accumulating, and partially forwarding of earth's continual, universal, energy income receipts. In addition, as we have learned from the International Geophysical Year, earth also receives about one hundred thousand tons of stardust daily. This randomly deposited dust apparently consists of all ninety-two chemical elements in approximately the same proportions as in the order of relative abundance of these elements in the thus far inventoried reaches of universe. Therefore, we are a collecting or concentrating center, possibly one among myriads in the universe. All planets in universe may be collecting points as focuses of the contracting phase of universe.

At the surface of the earth, in the top soil, the ecological balance becomes operative. The vegetation's chlorophyll inhibits the sun's radiation instead of allowing it to be reflectively rebroadcast back into universe. The sun-inhibited energy impounded in the vegetation is further inhibited by insects, worms, and mammals. Then both botanicals and zoologicals are gradually pressured into the growing earth crust until finally they are concentrated into the fossil fuels rather than being broadcast off to universe in all directions. My explorations of universe patternings make me afraid that by dissipating these energy concentrations man may well be upsetting the expansion-contraction balance of universe.

The ecological balance on earth is fascinating when viewed chemically. We find all biological systems continually sorting and rearranging atoms in methodical molecular structures. To insure performance, each species is genetically and environmentally programmed. Each one sorts and reassociates atoms as its genes cope with and alter environment and its produced reactions. This in turn alters species' behaviors. Biological life on earth is inherently anti-entropic for it negotiates the chemical sorting out of the earth's crust's chemical element inventory and rearranges the atoms in elegantly ordered molecular compound patternings. Earth is thus acting again as an anti-entropic center.

Of all the biological anti-entropics, i.e., random-to-orderly arrangers, man's intellect is by far the most active, exquisite, and effective agent thus far in evidence in universe. Through intellect, man constantly succeeds in inventing technological means of doing ever-more-orderly, more efficient, local universe energy tasks with ever less investments of the (what may only be apparently) "randomly" occurring resources of energy patterned as atomic matter or energy channeled as electro-magnetics.

I shall now recite to you some thoughts which I have had regarding information recently discovered by the neurologists' and physiologists' electrode probings of the brain. The brain probers have now identified, for instance, the location of various memory banks. Dr. Wilder Penfield, head of the Neurological Institute of McGill University in Montreal, Canada, says, "It is much easier to explain all the data we have regarding the brain if we assume an additional phenomenon 'mind' than it is to explain all the data if we assume only the existence of 'brain.'" Why? Because they have found, so to speak, the telephone sets of the brain, they have found the automatic message-answering service and the storage systems; but a great deal goes on in conversations over the wires that is not explicable by the physical brain's feedback. I have submitted what I am saying to you to leading neurologists and they have not found fault with it. A good scientist doesn't applaud you publicly or right away, even though he is favorably impressed with your theory. But he does let you know if he objects to what you are saying and then what his objections are. So far, I have received no objections and there seems to be some affirmation of what I am about to say to you.

There is a phenomenon that we call a "generalization." In science, a generalization is very different from a literary generalization. Generalization in the literary sense usually means that some statement is trying to cover too much territory. The scientific meaning is very precise: it means "the discovery and statement of a principle that holds true without exceptions." I will give you an example. I am going to talk about a special piece of rope. I could have in my hands a three-foot length of one-half-inch nylon rope or I could just as easily say to you, "I am going to take an imaginary piece of rope" and not mention material, lengths, or cross-section. This would be generalizing a rope concept from all our mutual rope experiences. Now I am going to pull on my rope very hard and as I pull on it, it will contract in its girth. As it gets tauter, it gets tighter. This means that it goes into compression in its girth in planes at ninety degrees to the axis of the pull. I have found a great many human beings who think that tension is something independent of compression. I find experimentally, however, that tension can only be operative when compression is also present. A cigar-shaped vertical compression member that is loaded on its neutral axis tries to "squash." This means that its girth tries to get bigger. Because it tries to get bigger, it expands and is therefore tensed. So I find that compression is never innocent of tension, but that they are cooperative in axes arranged at ninety degrees to one another. Sometimes I find tension at a maximum of "high tide" or highly visible aspect, and compression at a minimum or "low tide" or almost invisible aspect, and vice versa. This is a generalization. We have found by experiment that "tension and compression only coexist." That is quite an advance over the first generalization, "I take a piece of rope and pull on it," which was already a second-degree generalization. It is a third-degree generalization when I say "tension and compression only coexist."

A system divides universe into all of the universe that is outside the system and all of the universe that is inside the universe. Every system, as viewed from the inside, is concave and, as viewed from the outside, convex. Concave and convex only coexist. Concave and convex are very different one from the other. Convex diffuses energies by increasing wave lengths and widening angles. Concave concentrates energies by decreasing wave lengths and reducing angles. Although not the same and not exactly opposite, concave and convex can only coexist.

In addition to tension and compression, and concave and convex, I can give you a number of other such coexistences. This brings us then to another and further degree of generalization wherein we say that "there is a plurality of coexistent behaviors in nature which are the complementary behaviors." This caused the mathematicians to generalize still further. They developed the word "functions." "Functions" cannot exist by themselves. Functions only coexist with other functions. They are sometimes co-variables. When I say, "functions only coexist," I have gone a little further than the special cases of concave and convex of tension and compression which were themselves highly generalized. Then I can go further still and say, "unity is plural and at minimum two." This is the generalization which greatly advantaged quantum physics. We may go a little further in generalization as did Einstein when he gave us "relativity," which was discussed by Dr. Shapley. You can't have relativity without a plurality of cofunctions.

Now, I will give you another progression of events. You have seen a dog tugging at one end of a belt. He tenses the belt as he grips on it compressionally with the concave and convex surfaces of his teeth. Even though his brain is perfectly coordinating them, that little dog will never be able to say, "Tension and compression only coexist." The dog cannot say, "Concave and convex, tension and compression, are similar cases of coexistence of functions." I think the neurologists will go along with me in saying that, "What we mean by mind—in contradistinction to the brain of the animal or of man—is man's ability to generalize."

We have seen how an enormous amount of special case experiences finally led to a progression of generalizations. There were about six degrees of progressive generalization. As we went from one case to another and to higher degrees, it was accomplished with fewer and fewer words. We finally came to just one word, "relativity." Now this orderly simplification happens to be just the exact opposite of the mathematician's law of increase of the random element. It is the decrease of the random element. Generalization is the law of progressive orderliness.

The mind of man seems to be the most advanced phase of anti-entropy witnessable in universe. And if there is an expanding universe, there is logically a contracting universe. Possibly man's mind and his generalizations, which weigh nothing, operate at the most exquisite stage of universe contraction. Metaphysics balances physics. The physical portion of universe expands entropically. The metaphysical contracts anti-entropically. Man seems essential to the complementary functioning of universe.

BLAKESLEE: I want to accuse science fiction writers of being dangerous and malicious saboteurs—for me. My professional occupation is to try to keep up with advances in physical and biological sciences, and they are startling enough as it is. My mental filing cabinet at best is a little uncertain, so I don't dare read science fiction. It might cost me my job some day if I simply shrug my shoulders when somebody tells me that Martians have landed in Idaho and are stealing all the potatoes. I'll say, "Oh, sure, I knew that." Or when the mystery of Einstein's missing brain is resolved by a report that he is a student, that the brain has been transplanted to a young boy who is now grown up and a student at the University of Kansas and is failing in mathematics. I would know that, too. I wish I could read science fiction. Once in a while I've broken my pledge and have read some stories by Arthur Clarke and I have some loaned to me by your own Jim Gunn which I'm looking forward to reading. They are informative, ingenious, entertaining, and very often authentic, as you know.

One thing bothers me about space travel to other planets, and probably this has already been written in some science fiction story. It's the vision of the human race as a virus disease which has infected this planet, and which is now reaching out to infect another planet before we've first learned how to treat ours very kindly.

Science fiction writing can have its hilarious aspects. I've been fortunate to see a late movie twice which deals with the discovery by very intelligent American astronomers that something new in the sky is growing brighter and that this apparently is some planet, a strange planet, approaching earth. The scene switches to the White House where there's a council and the decision is made that the United States should do something about this before the Russians discover it's up in the sky. So within a very short time the space craft has been built—this movie was made quite some time before Sputnik—and they have chosen a crew of four. It turns out to be quite well balanced; there are two young men and two young ladies. Each one of these people should have special skills, so one is a physician, and they need a geologist so they pick one of the most famous geologists in the United States, and she turns out to be twenty-five years old. This leaves open to question where her fame arose, but anyhow she is made a member of the crew. So the day of the launching comes and they make their trip and land on this foreign planet, and this very intelligent doctor, after the ship has settled down on the planet, opens the hatch, sticks out his head, sniffs, and says: "It's okay. It does have an atmosphere." The best part is still to come. They explore the planet, of course, and during this process the other young lady tears her dress pretty high up on her thigh. They are engaged in a scientific exploration of this planet so at some point or another the girl geologist picks up a rock and begins to tap it with her little hammer as her companions eagerly gather around, and one of them says to her, "What is it?" She looks up and says about this rock, "It's prehistoric."

Arthur Clarke has been talking about a journey into the future, and it has been mentioned that exploration of the mind and the brain is one such concern, and one in which some progress is being made. In fact, there's a possibility within a very short time of the development of memory pills. This is based upon a theory that memory is encoded in RNA, which is a cousin of DNA. RNA could be the basis on which memory is stored in brain cells. And now some testing is underway in human patients of a drug which increases the production of RNA to learn whether this will stimulate learning processes and also memory retention. If it succeeds it would be a step toward having a memory pill, which I think would help most of us.

There also is some experimental evidence that we could be trained to forget. I think this might be very helpful to some of us when we have made great mistakes, when we have suffered embarrassments, or sometimes when you get some of your grades which you have won with your memory pills. There also may be some qualities of the brain that we know very little about yet, such as extrasensory perception. If we have and could apply such faculties perhaps we could tune in upon anyone else, anyplace else, at any time that we wished. There would be advantages in this form of human communication. It would save a lot of travel, time, and money. But like everything else that has been discussed here, there is that other side of the coin. Suppose the professor knew what you were thinking? I wonder whether Arthur Clarke with his fertile imagination would like to journey a little bit into what he expects may happen in this area in the coming years or decades.

BOWMAN: By design and plan I am the last one, at the moment at least, to talk to you, because my chore is to bring you back to earth and up out of the ocean depths. The title of Mr. Clarke's talk, as you noticed, was "Explorations in Tomorrow." Now tomorrow is not only a hundred years from now; tomorrow is also next week and next year, and there are a lot of useful things we could do presently if we would just be about it. They would make, technologically at least, our environment a little better than it is, which is really what we're attempting to do. Here, for example, are a few of the things we could do while we're waiting for means of traveling to the moon.

We could have cleaner streams, absolutely clean streams, if we wanted them. The pollution that we have in the air could be done away with. We could have highways where we could sit and read or play bridge as we drove along in a car controlled by an electric wire encased in the pavement. Salt water conversion to fresh water is a reality right now, of course. We even, frighteningly, have the chance of doing some things that may not be universally popular. For example, one could change the color of buildings automatically with the sun; wall louvers painted in different colors could be made to turn under different intensities of sunlight. For something more useful, I dare to hope that someone, whether engineer or scientist, will invent a soundproof partition wall for hotels and apartments. This is one of mankind's very great needs, and I'd like Bucky Fuller to focus on it sometime before he becomes too fascinated with moon travel.

But the other angle of this future is that we have accumulated so many scientific facts. We have been producing scientific data at such a prodigious pace in the last ten years that we actually don't know what we know about a great many things. One of the really important steps that we have to take is to store and retrieve this material, possibly using tapes and computers. We are working on this some, but, in the meantime, we are continuing to produce scientific data that the scientists themselves cannot keep track of. There are too many of them working on too many different things. When we have this inventory of knowledge in manageable form, we will be in a better position to accomplish some of the remarkable things that Mr. Clarke has foreseen. It isn't often that a person looks into the future with a perception as keen and a scientific background as complete as Mr. Clarke's. It makes us sit back and think, those of us who have always said that we're 100 per cent in favor of progress but don't like rapid change. There must be a lot of rapid change to bring about Mr. Clarke's forecasts.

CLARKE: I'd like to thank the panel for their very kind comments. They've dealt with me very gently and, in fact, I don't think they've given me any really difficult questions to answer. Of course, I didn't have any particular thesis in this talk. I was just throwing out ideas and trying to stir up some thoughts. I wasn't trying to predict the future; I was only indicating possible futures.

Mr. Fuller had some interesting things to say about the kind of freedom of living we would have, the ability to get on anywhere. That reminds me of something I might have mentioned. Back in 1927, I think, the crystallographer and physicist J. D. Bernal, in an extraordinary book, The World, The Flesh, and the Devil, suggested that man's real home was space, not the earth, because in space you could utilize the whole volume; there'd be no up or down; there would be a gravity-free

environment. And if you look at this room—how much of it
are we actually using now? Just this little skin. Try to
disorientate yourself for a moment: imagine that's the floor up
there and now imagine there's no floor, that all the walls anywhere are equally good. The efficiency of use of this volume at
the moment is, I suppose, about 5 per cent. Out in space
we could use any enclosed volume with complete efficiency.
And it has occurred to me, thinking along these lines, that maybe
our drive into space is an attempt to return to the weightless
environment in which we originated, that of the sea, where
again there is no sense of weight and the whole volume of space,
at least within very wide limits, can be utilized. I think you
get some psychological proof of this when you're skin diving;
when you're under water you leave all your worries and fears and
troubles behind you. It's impossible to worry under water; you
can be terrified but you can't worry. That's quite a distinction.

One thing I am rather scared of about these new potentialities
of living anywhere—and I'm sure it's a point that Dr. Eiseley
would make more eloquently than I could—is the danger of
losing the wilderness. Without nature, without the wilderness
to go back to occasionally, men's minds become fogged and
poisoned. You must get away from people occasionally. That's
another reason why I live in Ceylon, because there's a lot of
wilderness still there.

There was some mention of the developments in learning
techniques, particularly the work on DNA and RNA, and, of
course, you've heard the suggestion about professorburgers,
grinding up professors and feeding them to the students so the
information is passed on painlessly. Actually, of course, like
so many things, Swift had this idea in *Gulliver's Travels* in the
Laputa episode where, attempting to make fun of science, he
inadvertently described many things we're doing now.

I'd like to end with a definition. I've often been asked
during this seminar, what's the difference between fantasy
and science fiction? Perhaps this will throw some light on some
of the things I've already said. I say that fantasy is something
that couldn't possibly happen but you wish could happen,
whereas science fiction is something that could happen but you
hope that it won't.

MAN AND THE FUTURE | 9

THE CHANGED
AND CHANGING UNIVERSITY

Franklin D. Murphy

It is a fact that the winds of change are blowing in hurri-
cane fashion throughout the world. All men and all human
institutions are bound to be affected, and, at this point in
time, none is more touched by the storm than that ancient
institution called university.

The higher educational system of this country is creak-
ing and groaning under mid-twentieth-century strains. The
American people who are now crucially dependent upon the
health and vitality of this system must begin to attempt to
understand the genesis of these stresses so that instead of
merely flinging criticism at the system, they can participate
in guaranteeing its continued development.

The lack of understanding of our current problems is,
in my view, due to the fact that the adult members of our
society think of the university out of the conditioned reflexes of their own student experiences. Fifty years ago
the American college or university was, generally speaking,
a relatively isolated citadel of learning located on a small
tributary of the mainstream of society. To this citadel a very
limited number (5-10 per cent) of college-age youth went
to spend a few leisurely years with their teachers where, in
the process of obtaining a liberal education, they prepared

themselves to come down the tributary one day into the mainstream and bustle of human life. The quiet, unhurried tradition of university life was interrupted only by the excitement of the Saturday afternoon football game and the spring hijinks of goldfish swallowing or, in later days, panty raids. *In loco parentis* was mainly unchallenged. The primary concern of the institution was undergraduate teaching, and by and large this was done very well. Numbers were manageable, the knowledge to be communicated relatively simple, and the lot of regents, presidents, chancellors, and faculties relatively uncomplicated.

Now it is fifty years and a scientific, technological revolution later, and what are the responsibilities of the American university today?

In the first instance, we still have the central obligation of teaching undergraduate students but undergraduate students in such numbers as were never dreamed of before. Not only are there many more young people in absolute numbers, but now well over one-third of these young people are determined to seek education beyond the high school. In addition, the body of knowledge to be communicated has become infinitely more complex. There is little relationship between the physics of a half century ago and the nuances of that field which must be communicated today. The same can be said of all of the academic disciplines. The shrinkage of the world in point of time and distance has led to the total relevance of a full understanding of the cultures and languages of non-Western societies.

To complicate the matter further, the growth of graduate study has been exponential. Large and growing numbers of young men and women now seek education beyond the baccalaureate degree, and this is the kind of education which requires teaching in depth and in unusual concentration with ever more complicated laboratories and massive research library collections.

If the explosion in numbers of students, types of students, and the complexity of knowledge to be communicated was alone the measure of increased responsibilities of the university, we would be very pressed in any event. But this is just one aspect of its expanded obligations, for this venerable institution has now been brought out of its relative isolation on the tributary and placed squarely in the mainstream of society to a degree that not even the creators of the "land-grant college" tradition could have conceived.

The University has, of course, been a central force in another explosion, that of knowledge, and it cannot disengage itself. On the contrary, as the tempo of discovery proceeds even more rapidly, the university is ever more intimately involved because of the critical impact of discovery on all aspects of the life of the society.

It is now crystal clear that our national security is overwhelmingly dependent on university research laboratories and the scientists and students who labor therein. Beyond this, the competence of our government in the management of science in the best interests of the whole society requires the constant, indeed growing, advice and counsel of members of the academic community; hence the central role of the Science Advisory Committee to the President of the United States, and the whole range of other kinds of advisory commissions to the Secretary of Defense, the Atomic Energy Commission and the National Aeronautics and Space Administration, to name but a few.

But the effective leadership of the United States in this troubled and revolutionary world is related to other matters just as important as military strength. The Secretary of State, in creating and assessing foreign policy, needs and now seeks the advice and counsel of university experts along

282 | Franklin D. Murphy

a broad range of interests and expertise. The Agency for International Development, representing the fourth and newest component of American foreign policy—educational and cultural development overseas—has been dependent on the American university and its faculties in building new universities and professional schools all over the world or in helping to expand and modernize existing ones.

We have only to look inward, however, within the United States itself, to identify another new and important responsibility of our universities and their faculties. The economic growth of this country, involving the central problem of jobs for an expanding population and the continued economic vitality of our society, is intimately related to this research effort. New products and new techniques come from new knowledge, and it is only new products and new techniques which will keep the economy expanding. Thus, the American business and industrial establishment now accepts without reservation its great dependence on the American university and its productivity, both in the fields of research and in training sophisticated manpower. Beyond this, university economists are asked to advise the President of the United States, Cabinet officers, industry, and labor unions alike.

Federal, state, and local governments in an unprecedented fashion turn now to the American university for the expert advice required to solve some of the critical problems of a rapidly expanding population concentrated more and more in the new phenomenon of megalopolis. Hundreds of thousands of academic man-hours are going into crucial efforts concerned with the prevention of air and water pollution, desalting sea water, transportation of people within the urban complex, public health, slum clearance, human relations, and the preservation of what little beauty is left in this badly exploited nation of ours. In increasing numbers the American people are comprehending that dependence on laissez faire and what grandfather did can only lead to a kind of urban suicide, and that it is to the university and its scholars they must turn for many of the solutions to these new and complicated problems.

If this were not enough, one must remember that the volume of new knowledge and the shrinkage of the world have put a burden in time and urgency of unprecedented proportions on the faculty member himself in terms of his professional development and the requirements laid upon him to become and remain up-to-date in his knowledge. One cannot talk or teach about Africa or any other part of the world without having been there, and, in many instances, becoming fluent in what are thought of as bizarre and exotic languages. And so, the faculty member, in order merely to retain his competence as a teacher of relevant knowledge, must more often than ever before go to the appropriate laboratory, which is not on campus but thousands of miles distant, and there spend time in study and research. Were he not to do this, he might as well substitute the current issue of the *Encyclopedia Britannica* for his classroom presentations.

And then if all of this were not enough, consider the growing demands of an ever more educated adult society on the university for continuing education. The explosion in knowledge, the rapidly changing techniques of dealing with society and its problems, and the complexities of the great problems of our time have led to a remarkable increase in demands on the university to provide a variety of formal classroom and lecture experiences for those already holding a university degree. Classroom and lecture halls are as full at night as in the daytime with thousands of people, most not seeking a degree or a grade, but simply answers to questions that did not exist yesterday.

The foregoing represents a substantial, but not complete, list of what society has, in less than a half century and with great insistence, added to the responsibilities of the modern American university. Which of these responsibilities does any thoughtful man think we should now eliminate?

Shall we withdraw from our central role in the security of our nation? Shall we turn our back on the economic development of our country? Shall we tell the adults in our population that we do not have time to expand their expertise and knowledge? Shall we declare that we have no interest in expanding the effectiveness and precision of American foreign policymaking? Are we to forget about clean air and pure and adequate water for an expanding society? Shall we accept the notion that the human relations issues of our day are insoluble?

Yet, on the other hand, dare we turn our back on any motivated and competent young man or woman who seeks higher educational opportunity and thus destroy one of the central traditions of this great nation? Are we to admit that since the university cannot withdraw from its central role in the great issues of the day, it must, for the foreseeable future, condemn the student to an inadequate education by virtue of a lack of interest, lack of time, lack of well-trained teachers, lack of facilities, or a combination of all?

The fact is, of course, that at this extraordinary point in human history the university cannot withdraw from any of these obligations but must expect even more responsibilities in the future. To think otherwise would demonstrate unforgivable irresponsibility. The unavoidable answer is not to reduce the obligations of the university, but, rather, to provide resources and manpower to permit it to meet *all* of these obligations and meet them well.

Presently, we in American higher education are in the

position of trying to fill a gallon jug with not much more than a quart of water. Such an exercise is bound to lead to frustration, with a feeling on the part of all of the consumers of the university that they are not being adequately served. And they are right. But, at the same time, they should understand that this imperfect performance is not a matter of intent, but rather a matter of resources unequal to the explosion of expectations.

No one should be surprised at the creaks and groans in the university today. By tradition and by performance, the university has been the miner, the refiner, and purveyor of knowledge—always important to the evolution of society, now perhaps crucial to its survival. The exponential growth of its obligations has led to great changes in its structure and function and relationship to society. Yet, great as these changes have been, I believe they are but a prelude to greater changes still to come. As the forces of the twentieth-century revolution continue to build, the university will move ever closer to the center of the ferment. Involvement and interaction will grow, and the inevitable result will be great change, both in the society and in the university.

Only a foolhardy man would dare to predict even the immediate future with a claim to certitude. But some realities with long-term implications are already on us. Perhaps the one with the greatest consequences is the rapidly growing involvement of the federal government in educational financing and curricular emphasis. Federal support of higher education has, of course, been with us for over one hundred years—from the implementation of the Morrill Act in 1863. The harmonious relationship of our land-grant colleges and universities to their benefactor, the United States government, over a century of remarkable institutional growth and development, provides little support for the view that federal involvement in higher education is necessarily debilitating.

However, these so-called land-grant funds were but a trickle compared to the torrents of dollars which began to flow from government to higher education at the end of World War II, primarily in support of research. From the National Institute of Health, the several military services, the Atomic Energy Commission, the National Science Foundation, and more recently, the National Aeronautics and Space Administration, literally billions of dollars have been infused into the bloodstream of our universities and with such speed and in such unprecedented volume as to raise real questions concerning the effect of such a massive infusion on the chemical balance of the receiving institutions. The two worlds of C. P. Snow seem to have been driven even farther apart. The balance between teaching and investigation has clearly been altered, a fact to which an ever-growing number of restless, resentful, and now vocal students are beginning to attest. The harmonious and relatively simple relationships between government and university characterizing the period of the land-grant subventions have become strained and complicated.

And now, having managed to resolve or rationalize constitutional questions, the Congress has made the final commitment for major support for higher education per se. No longer will such support be bootlegged through the back door in the name of research or defense. The nation has decided, for better or for worse, that the federal government will become a full and permanent partner in the support of all aspects of American higher education.

The most obvious effect of this historic decision is the availability of a new and large source of financial support. The first reaction of the academic community is one of undisguised pleasure. The hard-pressed administrator, faced with the need for more of everything, sees significant relief. The faculty can envisage better tools and a more adequate workshop, to say nothing of appropriate compensation. The student, pressed by increased educational costs and a longer learning experience, finds real hope in more funds for fellowships, scholarships, and loans. And the educational philosopher may begin to believe again that the university can indeed serve all of the needs of society and still retain the time-honored American tradition of the broadest educational opportunity for all.

For those who would challenge the propriety and rationale for the intervention of the federal government in these matters, there is also a logical answer beyond the immediately apparent one of just plain financial need. The answer goes to the obvious point that the national government is the only instrument that can effectively serve a truly *national* need. The federal land grants were based on the interest of the whole country in a *national* agricultural and industrial development. The need was a national one—the instrumentality was the state university—and so a logical marriage was consummated.

Again, when after World War II the national need for new knowledge got into public consciousness, it was the federal government that had the obligation and resources to match the need. The universities had the manpower, and so a new partnership was forged in the interest of building a national research competence and a body of new knowledge to serve the whole society.

Now the state of these complex and revolutionary days dictates that the further development of this country and the discharge of our obligations to the world society, to say nothing of our survival itself, depend on maximal development of all of our human resources and a remarkable expansion of the national pool of trained and educated manpower. As is ever the case, the national interest must come first, and, in this instance, it can be adequately served in these times only by the resources and commitment of the whole nation.

Yet, given the philosophic and pragmatic logic of significant federal support for higher education, there remains much which should concern the educational community in the creation of a proper relationship between government and educational institutions. This should be a full and equal partnership, but recent, and, unhappily, continuing experience tells us that there is often a tendency for the government partner to want to become more than equal with the university. To put it more plainly, as American higher education and the United States government move to join hands in a major effort, the contract must be drawn in such a way as to guarantee the proper independence of the university and the freedom to the community of scholars to chart their own course with responsibility and wisdom.

It is a happy coincidence that during the critical period when the basic contracts are being drawn men of the caliber of John Gardner and Frank Keppel are representing the government. So much depends on the quality, imagination, and understanding of the governmental administrative mechanism. The contracts may be drawn with wisdom, but if in subsequent years the contracts are interpreted by third-rate and rigid minds, we are all in for much trouble, administratively and educationally. It is clear that all of us in education must do our utmost to assist Mr. Gardner in staffing the new administrative posts within the Department of Health, Education, and Welfare with creative men and women as appropriate. We must all be willing to serve faithfully and forcefully on the several advisory bodies to the new federal programs with the determination to see that higher education's advice is, in fact, heeded.

You may wonder why I have devoted so much of my time to the general subject of the growing role of the federal government in American higher education. It is because I think it provides greater promise, although it requires greater continuing scrutiny, than any event affecting higher education within the last century. Let us turn to some examples of the promise.

Since World War II, the relatively unprepared American university has been thrust quite literally into the whole world. We have been asked to build new universities in developing countries and help invigorate old universities in established societies. Our scholars have had and have accepted unparalleled opportunities to explore and study all of the world's cultures, not in the library but on the spot. In short, a new dimension has been given to the concept of an international community of scholars. But the effort has been imperfect, often inadequate, relatively unplanned, and too short-range in character. Now a generally friendly Congress has before it the President's message on international education and implementing legislation. The legislation provides funds to build more and better centers of research and advanced training in international affairs. It proposes funds to vitalize undergraduate studies concerning the entire spectrum of non-United States cultures. The Presidential message itself instructs the Secretary of Health, Education, and Welfare to establish in his Department a Center for Educational Cooperation with an advisory council on International Education.

At long last we have a proposal to regularize on a long term basis the role of the American university in world affairs and to provide adequate funding therefor. The Bill now before Congress, called the International Education Act of 1966, is clearly in the mid-twentieth century—in terms of the realities of today the equivalent of the land-grant act in the realities of the mid-nineteenth century. The potentialities of achievement are quite as great.

So much is said about the explosion of knowledge these days that the phrase has almost become a cliché—but not to the librarian, inundated as he is by an ever-increasing torrent of words, journals, and books. And what about the scholar who, for all his inventive genius, still can find only twenty-four hours per day, all of which he cannot devote to a search of the literature? The only answer is a national, or, at the very least, a few regional centers where this flood of information is stored on tape immediately available by telecommunication to the scholar. No single university and its library can accomplish this, and no regional group of universities, no matter how cooperative, can do it well. Only a national network, conceived and directed by university-based people, can possibly come to grips with the information-retrieval problem. The day is certainly not far off when every serious scholar in this country will have almost literally at his fingertips much of the current body of knowledge he seeks—and this because the federal government can help do for us what we cannot do each for himself.

The concept of a national network of information retrieval centers leads logically to the notion of institutional sharing of resources and responsibilities on a national or regional basis. Some such efforts evolved historically, as with the nine campuses within the system of higher education called the University of California. More recently, the enormous cost of basic research equipment, such as radio telescopes and nuclear accelerators, has led to consortia of universities in some kind of corporate relationship sharing the management responsibility rather than one institution alone. Here within the so-called Big Eight group of universities within the Big Ten, among groupings of four-year liberal arts colleges in many parts of the country, in the

Rocky Mountain states and in the South, a variety of cooperative enterprises has been developed involving certain professional curricula, overseas programs, and joint use of specialized equipment or other resources. In short, there is an accelerating awakening to the fact that today no institution, no matter how strong, can or should try to do everything well and by itself. Old school pride cannot encompass the vast and growing boundaries of current and future intellectual activity. It is my firm conviction that one of the most sophisticated uses of the newly available federal funds for higher education should be the support of soundly conceived and imaginative cooperative and regional programs involving several institutions. Here is a major educational highway to the future.

Discussion of regional and national programs of higher educational cooperation leads naturally to a consideration of the problem of the several states in integrating their own programs in education beyond the high school. It is clear that no state can leave its higher educational development to laissez faire or to the Chamber of Commerce and political pressures. This is just too expensive and wasteful of severely limited manpower. Furthermore, it is the road to poor quality which does not add to the national image of the state. There must be a reasonably sophisticated and well-informed mechanism for planning and for giving educational advice to the state government. In my view, today most states, and in the near future all states, will have to develop a plan which keeps educational doors open but which brings students and faculty together in homogeneous groups based on motivation, native ability, and professional aspiration. No state has yet found the perfect answer. But I venture to predict that as the answer evolves most state university campuses, not excepting this one, will look quite different from yesteryear, with an ultimate enrollment limitation and, within that limitation, priority given to graduate, professional, and upper-division students. The corollary is, of course, that at that point other no-less-important institutions or campuses will be in the field with a primary concern for lower-division collegiate work of very high quality. In this matter, as in all others, the educator has got to deal with realities of today and tomorrow, uninfluenced by tradition and the presumed validities of the recent past.

But how does the university community deal with the onrushing events of our time and the days just ahead? This matter turns on the governance of the institution and here there is much to be done. The basic fact is that most, if not all, American universities are underadministrated. The number of gifted and experienced people available to give administrative guidance to what have become multimillion dollar complicated corporate entities, dealing with a wide range of governmental and private agencies, foreign governments, a large corps of sophisticated scholars, and an ever-increasing number of ever-more-demanding students, simply does not match the need. There are historical reasons for this, mainly related to the remarkable speed with which the university has grown and changed. But there are still those who hold that the best university administration is the least. In fact, on one of our most distinguished American university campuses, within this decade, the chief administrative officer could belligerently assert that he was primarily a scholar, not an administrator, and that he was, under all circumstances, going to save half of his work week for his laboratory. This he did, but it was probably not coincidental that a few years later this campus suffered one of the worst convulsions in American higher educational history. On this same campus an enormous amount of the business of the university was carried on by the faculty. The number of hours devoted to committee work by large numbers of this faculty simply defies description—much, if not all, of it falling in the category of just busy work. No wonder the students couldn't find the faculty. This kind of a situation, presumably related to some kind of medieval nostalgia, is not just inadequate—it represents an irresponsible wastage of an all-too-limited pool of teaching, research, and student-advising talent.

President James Perkins, in his recent Little lectures at Princeton, says, "The University can never again run on the assumption that it commands or can command the full-time interest and attention of all its faculty. The nature of knowledge today is such that it requires minds and talents of quite a different order from those needed to make administrative decisions. And the faculty should be left as free as possible of administrative duties in order to do its work."

This is, of course, not to gainsay the crucial participation of faculty members in the dialogue leading to important policy decisions and selection of new and evaluation of existing faculty members, for example. What I am saying, however, is that one of the most important bits of business before higher education today has to do with streamlining and strengthening its administrative structure and recruiting the best people in adequate numbers to its administrative posts on a full-time basis. Without such strengthened management, the American university will at best only founder and conceivably drown in the rapidly rising tide of the demands of society.

To now we have discussed many facets of the changing university world—but what of the *raison d'être* of the whole establishment, the student? What with administrative problems, carrying education to the rest of the world, research, scholarly travel, and government advisement, will there be any energy left for him? Well, if he has anything to say about it, there will be—and he has much to say and is saying it loudly these days. For as society and the university have changed, so have our students. They are older because they come to us later and they stay with us longer. They are better prepared, Admiral Rickover to the contrary notwithstanding. They are the product of a permissive tradition. Most have had more independence and freedom in their high school years than my generation had in the university. The revolution in communications has made them aware of the world and its problems in an unprecedented fashion. They are products of an age of revolution and rapidly changing verities and social benchmarks. They share with all society the uncertainties and insecurities of a world in turmoil and torment. Is it any wonder they refuse to be put in a sandbox to play the innocent game traditionally called "student activities," properly insulated from involvement in the major problems of society? The American university student has left the sandbox for good, just as he has rejected *in loco parentis* as irrelevant to one who could be fighting in Vietnam any day now. And I must say that I, for one, understand and applaud this.

If Vietnam, civil rights, foreign policy, birth control, and treatment of migrant workers are matters with which society must deal, then this generation of students intends to be involved. Sometimes the characteristic candor of youth irritates the conscience of the elder, and energy may temporarily be substituted for direction. Occasional exhibitionists may blur the image (remember the goldfish swallowers of the 1920's and the panty raiders of the 1950's, and the righteous indignation they produced). But at least (and how wonderful) they are concerned, and they are involved.

The university student is out of the sandbox never to return. Society will just have to adjust to it. The university community will need to talk with him too—and about substantive matters. He does not want to run the university. But he believes he has something useful to contribute to the dialogue. He wants to talk about the important issues of curriculum, the rewards for good teaching, and the proper relationship between teaching and research. He has always been told he was an important member of the academic community, and he has now determined to assume that role. I believe that this change in student attitude is one of the best things that could have happened to American higher education. It will become an indispensable element in preventing administration and faculty from taking things for granted. It will contribute mightily to a lively and student-oriented curriculum. The university dialogue will become enriched and more germane as a result. And a strong and more mature student voice will become a great force in reminding us all of the time-honored importance of teaching.

I have this morning dealt only with a few aspects of change within the American university, those things which are most on my mind at the moment. One could, of course, discuss many other important trends and directions: the emergence of the fine arts, including the performing aspects, as full and respectable members of the academic community; the inevitability of greater blurring of the lines between the last years of the secondary school and the first college years and an even greater overlap between the senior year of college and the first year of graduate study; the desirability and inevitability of more independent undergraduate study; the likelihood that all professional studies, not excluding education, engineering, and business administration, will become graduate programs, following a four-year general undergraduate experience. But a combination of the revolution of today and tomorrow and the central role of the university in our society makes a listing of possible changes limitless, and I do not propose to posture as an encyclopedic seer.

Let me close then by saying that in the past one hundred years an amazing mix of gifted scholars, motivated students, a philosophy of education primarily rooted in quality, all surrounded by the indefinable Kansas ambiance, have combined to create a remarkable tradition. It is this tradition more than anything else which assures that the University of Kansas can move into the twenty-first century, now only thirty-four years away, with the certainty that whatever the future, this institution will meet it with enthusiasm and success. The Reverend Oliver, General Fraser, and Francis Huntington Snow built better than even they dared to dream, and the end is not yet in sight.

THE INTER-CENTURY
SEMINAR PARTICIPANTS

PHILIP H. ABELSON

Co-discoverer of the element Neptunium, co-inventor of a uranium isotope separation method that helped make possible the atom bomb, Philip Abelson is editor of *Science* Magazine, weekly journal of the American Association for the Advancement of Science. He was born in Tacoma, Washington, in 1913, and earned his B.S. from Washington State College and his M.S. and Ph.D. in nuclear physics from the University of California (Berkeley), the latter in 1939. He joined the staff of the Carnegie Institution of Washington, D.C., in 1939 and performed basic research which led in 1940 to the identification of Neptunium. As physicist for the Naval Research Laboratory during World War II, he helped develop the liquid thermal diffusion process for the separation of uranium isotopes. He also drew up plans which led to the eventual development of the atomic-powered submarine. In 1962 he assumed editorship of *Science* on the condition that he not be required to give up his other interests, and he has made that publication a lively source of the latest information and speculations about science, as well as a platform for editorial leadership.

ALTON L. BLAKESLEE

Science writer Alton Blakeslee was born in Dallas, Texas, in 1913; after studies at Duke University, he received his A.B. from Columbia University in 1935. He worked as a reporter on a Wilmington, Delaware, newspaper before joining the Associated Press in 1939. He served as a foreign correspondent during World War II and turned to science writing in 1946. He was a correspondent on the U.S. Navy Antarctic Expedition of 1946-47 and has won many awards since then for his coverage as science writer for the Associated Press. He has written several books, including *Polio and the Salk Vaccine*, *What You Should Know About Heart Disease*, and *Your Heart Has Nine Lives*.

WALDO G. BOWMAN

Born in 1900 in Lawrence, Kansas, Waldo Bowman earned his baccalaureate degree in civil engineering from the University of Kansas in 1923 and then attended the Harvard Graduate School of Business. After working as a structural designer for the Chicago Bridge and Iron Company and then the Boston Bridge Works, he began his long service with the *Engineering News-Record* in 1925. He served as editor from 1940 until his retirement in 1964.

ARTHUR C. CLARKE

One of the best-known science fiction and science writers, Arthur C. Clarke was born in Minehead, Somersetshire, England, in 1917. He earned a B.Sc. from the University of London in 1948 after eight years as an auditor in the British Civil Service, began writing science fiction, served as a radar instructor in the Royal Air Force, and was elected chairman of the British Interplanetary Society. He served as assistant editor of *Science Abstracts* from 1949-50 and became a full-time freelance writer in 1951. Among his books of fiction are: *The Sands of Mars, Childhood's End, Against the Fall of Night, Prelude to Space, The Deep Range,* and *A Fall of Moondust.* In non-fiction, he has written: *Interplanetary Flight, The Exploration of Space, The Coast of Coral, The Challenge of the Spaceship, Profiles of the Future,* and many others. Most recently he collaborated with Stanley Kubrick on the motion picture and book, *2001: A Space Odyssey.* He is credited with being the first to propose a practical method for communication by satellite, in 1945 in an article in *Wireless World.* He now lives in Colombo, Ceylon.

HAROLD E. CLURMAN

Director and producer Harold Clurman was born in New York City in 1901. He attended Columbia University and earned his degree in letters from the Sorbonne, University of Paris, in 1923. After five years as actor and stage manager for the Theatre Guild and two years as a play reader, he helped found the famed Group Theatre and helped direct many of the plays of Clifford Odets, William Saroyan, Eugene O'Neill, Arthur Miller, and others. From 1941-45 he was a motion picture producer and director before returning to stage work. He also has contributed substantially to the literature of the theater, with monthly columns, criticism, and books such as *The Fervent Years* and *Lies Like Truth*.

LOREN C. EISELEY

Anthropologist Loren C. Eiseley was born in Lincoln, Nebraska, in 1907. He earned his A.B. from the University of Nebraska in 1933 and his A.M. and Ph.D. from the University of Pennsylvania, the latter in 1937. He served on paleontological expeditions from 1931 to 1933 and in 1934 and 1935. In 1937 he accepted the position of assistant professor of sociology and anthropology at the University of Kansas. From 1944-47 he served as chairman of sociology and anthropology at Oberlin College and then occupied a similar post at the University of Pennsylvania. There he served as Provost from 1959-61, and since that time as chairman of the department and University Professor of the history and philosophy of science. He is perhaps best known as the author of books such as *The Immense Journey* and *The Firmament of Time*, combining scholarship in anthropology and the history of science with poetic diction and prophetic insight.

R. BUCKMINSTER FULLER

Called "the first poet of technology," Buckminster Fuller was born in Milton, Massachusetts, in 1895. A student at Harvard for two years and at the U.S. Naval Academy for one, Fuller worked at a variety of occupations before finding his proper field of innovation. He worked as an apprentice machine-fitter for a cotton mill machine importer, in various apprentice positions and then as assistant export manager for Armour & Co. in New York City, as president of the Stockage Building System, as founder and president of the 4-D Company of Chicago. He invented the Dymaxion House in 1927 and, after such other inventions as the Dymaxion three-wheeled car, the geodesic dome in 1954. Author, philosopher, idea generator, Fuller has been described as "the greatest living genius of industrial-technical realization in building" and "an anticipator of the world to come." He now is a research scholar at Southern Illinois University.

ERIC LARRABEE

The managing editor of *Horizon* Magazine was born in 1922 in Melrose, Massachusetts. He earned his B.A. from Harvard in 1943, served in the U.S. Army for three years, and became associate editor of *Harper's* Magazine, serving from 1946-58. In 1958 he became executive editor of *American Heritage* and managing editor in 1960 before joining *Horizon*. He is the author of *The Self-Conscious Society* and the editor of *American Panorama, Mass Leisure,* and *American Perspectives.* In 1967 he was appointed Provost for Arts and Letters of the State University of New York at Buffalo.

ARTHUR LARSON

Lawyer, educator, federal administrator, Arthur Larson was born in Sioux Falls, South Dakota, in 1910. He earned his baccalaureate degree from Augustana College in 1931 and spent three years at Oxford University as a Rhodes Scholar, earning four degrees, including the Doctor of Civil Laws. After practicing law in Milwaukee, he taught in the Law Schools of the University of Tennessee, Cornell, and Pittsburgh, where he was Dean. He left Pittsburgh to become Under Secretary of Labor in 1954. In 1956 he was appointed director of the U.S. Information Agency, and in 1957 special assistant to President Eisenhower. After leaving Washington he continued as part-time special consultant to the President and is consultant to President Johnson on international affairs and to the State Department on United Nations matters. Since 1958 he has been director of the Rule of Law Research Center at Duke University.

DEANE W. MALOTT

Born in Abilene, Kansas, in 1898, Deane W. Malott earned his baccalaureate degree from the University of Kansas and his M.B.A. from the Harvard School of Business. Immediately after his graduation from Harvard, he took up duties as assistant dean of the Harvard School of Business and served in that position from 1923-1929. He was vice-president of the Hawaiian Pineapple Company from 1929-33 before returning to Harvard as associate professor in the School of Business. In 1939 he was offered the position of Chancellor of the University of Kansas and served until 1951. During his tenure, which covered the difficult war years, the enrollment of the University doubled, the size of the faculty tripled, and private gifts increased spectacularly. Chancellor and Mrs. Malott also were deeply interested in campus landscaping and beautification. In 1951 Chancellor Malott accepted the presidency of Cornell University, where he served until his retirement in 1963.

KARL A. MENNINGER

A pioneer in the field of mental health and the training of psychiatrists, Dr. Karl Menninger was born in 1893 in Topeka, Kansas. After attending Washburn University and Indiana University, he obtained his A.B. and his M.S. from the University of Wisconsin and his M.D. from Harvard University in 1917. Following an internship in Kansas City, practice in the Boston Psychopathic Hospital, and teaching in the Harvard Medical School, he returned to Topeka to practice with his father. There, joined by his brother William, and then other doctors, they developed a psychiatric group practice or clinic from which the Menninger Foundation grew. A prolific author, Dr. Menninger also devoted himself to public problems, assisting with the organization of the Veterans Administration training program for psychiatrists at Topeka and a similar program at Topeka State Hospital, together composing the Menninger School of Psychiatry, now the largest training center for psychiatrists in the world. He helped bring Kansas from next to last among the states in mental health to first.

ASHLEY MONTAGU

Born in London in 1905, Ashley Montagu was a student at the University of London and the University of Florence before earning his Ph.D. at Columbia University in 1937. He has been curator of physical anthropology at the Wellcome Historical Medical Museum, assistant professor of anatomy at New York University, associate professor of anatomy at Hahnemann Medical College and Hospital, and chairman of the department of anthropology at Rutgers University. He is a prolific author, his publications including *On Being Human*, *On Being Intelligent*, *The Natural Superiority of Women*, and *Man: His First Million Years*.

FRANKLIN D. MURPHY

Born in 1916 in Kansas City, Missouri, Franklin D. Murphy earned his baccalaureate degree from the University of Kansas in 1936 and his M.D. degree from the University of Pennsylvania in 1941. After three years of post-graduate work in internal medicine at the University of Pennsylvania and service in the U.S. Army, he became dean of the University of Kansas School of Medicine in 1948 where he developed the famous Kansas Rural Health Plan and was selected in 1949 by the U.S. Junior Chamber of Commerce as one of the ten outstanding young men in the nation. In 1951 he succeeded Deane W. Malott as Chancellor of the University of Kansas, where he helped initiate or intensify such programs as endowed professorships, gifted student programs, international education, and growth in library holdings and endowment as well as enrollment and campus facilities.

HARLOW SHAPLEY

A star-gazer who developed a yard-stick for the universe, Harlow Shapley was born in Nashville, Missouri, in 1885. He earned his A.B. and his A.M. from the University of Missouri and his Ph.D. in astronomy from Princeton University in 1913. For seven years he was an astronomer at the Mount Wilson Observatory in California before accepting the positions of Paine Professor of astronomy at Harvard University and director of the Harvard Observatory, which he held for 35 and 31 years respectively, before retirement. He helped develop many of the concepts and means by which distances between stars and sizes of galaxies were calculated and has received world-wide recognition and acclaim. He has written such books as *The Inner Metagalaxy, Of Stars and Men,* and *The View from a Distant Star.*

ROBERT LEWIS SHAYON

Writer, producer, director, critic, Robert Lewis Shayon is equally at home on both sides of the radio or television set. Born in New York City, he began his career in radio as a producer-director for the Mutual Broadcasting System in 1938. In 1942 he went with the Columbia Broadcasting System as an executive producer, where he is credited with developing the "You Are There" technique. He worked for a year as radio-television critic for *The Christian Science Monitor* and then took up his present duties as radio-television critic and feature writer for the *Saturday Review.* He has written, produced, directed, and narrated radio and television documentaries, winning the Peabody Award and the New York Radio Critics Circle Award in 1948 and the School Bell award of the National Education Association in 1960. He is the author of *The Eighth Art*.

W. CLARKE WESCOE

The present Chancellor of the University of Kansas, who moderated the Inter-Century Seminar, was born in Allentown, Pennsylvania, in 1920. After earning his B.S. in 1941 from Muhlenberg College and his M.D. in 1944 from Cornell University, he interned at the Cornell Medical Center and served for two years in the U.S. Army Medical Corps. From 1948-51 he served as instructor and assistant professor in pharmacology at Cornell University Medical College before coming to the University of Kansas in 1951 as professor of pharmacology and experimental medicine. The following year he became Dean of the School of Medicine and Director of the Medical Center. In 1960 he accepted the position of Chancellor.

CHARLES E. WHITTAKER

Born in 1901 on a farm near Troy, Kansas, Charles E. Whittaker attended public schools in Kansas. He earned his law degree in 1924 from the Kansas City School of Law (now the University of Missouri at Kansas City) and joined the Kansas City law firm for which he had worked as an office boy. He became a full member of that firm, then known as Watson, Ess, Whittaker, Marshall & Enggas, specializing in trial work until about 1942 and thereafter in appellate work and other legal matters. In 1954 he was appointed U.S. District Judge by President Eisenhower, to the U.S. Court of Appeals in 1956, and to the U.S. Supreme Court in 1957. For health reasons he retired in 1962 but still remains a Justice and may serve on any other federal court as needed and assigned. He lives in Kansas City, Missouri.